The Healing Force
of
Serenity

Integrating Eastern and Western Medicine
In The Maintenance and Recovery Of Health

Diane Lau Cordrey, Ph.D.

Century Press
Thomaston, Maine

ISBN 0-89754-195-2

Self-help $15.95

To The Reader

The techniques and suggestions in this book are not designed to replace traditional medical treatment. They are suggested to complement whatever treatment the patient is currently receiving and to maximize healing potential through participating in good health choices. Any activities or life-style changes described should be implemented under the guidance of a health-care practitioner. The intent of the author is only to provide general information to assist you in your search for good health. The author and publisher cannot be held responsible for any outcomes of implementing approaches discussed therein.

Century Press
PO Box 298
Thomaston, Maine 04861
U.S.A.

To
My Children
And
To Theirs

Acknowledgments

The anecdotal situations in this book are true. The people whose stories have been told are composites of patients and clients from my practice of more than twenty-five years. Names and places have been changed to insure confidentiality. Although I have spoken to all of you whose stories I used, I would like to thank you again for your willingness to share your experiences. I would also like to extend my sincere appreciation to everyone who has contributed time and energy to helping me bring this project to fruition.

Sheldon Kramer, Ph.D. encouraged me to expand my thinking and to focus on excellence. Buzz Baker, Ph.D. provided insight and inspiration with his sagacious comments and gentle goading. David Wang clarified much of the Chinese thinking, epitomizing the quintessential Qigong practitioner with his calm and gentle ways.

Harvey Kurland, my first teacher of Taijiquan, inspired my continual study. He also read the section on Chinese medicine and made valuable suggestions.

Joanne Howard motivates, not only me, but so many of the students in her fitness classes to improve and maintain their health through movement and connecting with others.

... and a very special thank you to my husband, Gary, who read countless revisions of the manuscript, photographed the scene on the cover and continues to nurture my heart.

Romanization Of Chinese Words

The author uses the Pinyin method of romanizing Chinese to English. Pinyin is the standard system used in the People's Republic of China and in most world organizations including the United Nations. Pinyin was introduced in China in the 1950s, replacing the Wade-Giles and the Yale systems.

Most of the pronunciations are similar to that of the English language except for the following exceptions: *q* is pronounced roughly like *ch*, *x* like *sh*, *c* like *ts* in "its", and *zh* like *j* in "jam."

Examples:

Pinyin	Also spelled as	Pronunciation
Qi	Chi	chee
Qigong	Chi Kung	chee kung
Gongfu	Kung Fu	gong fu
Taijiquan	Tai Chi Chuan	tai jee chuen

Introduction

The November evening was cool and pleasant but it did nothing to alleviate my apathetic mood. Halfheartedly, I tossed clothes into a suitcase for the trip to my parents' house in Northern California. In past years, I had always looked forward to this long Thanksgiving weekend with my large extended Chinese family. It had always been heartwarming to spend time with my parents, brother, aunts, uncles and cousins.

My cousins and I are typical of third generation Chinese in America. We have Western educations and speak English fluently, with little knowledge of the Chinese language. We view ourselves as completely enculturated into the society of our great-grandparents' adopted country. Some of us married Caucasians. Our favorite foods include hamburgers, steaks, mashed potatoes. We ascribe to Western medicine and health care and I, particularly, as a clinical psychologist trained in Western thought, disdained the practices of my ancestors and the precepts of traditional Chinese medicine.

On this specific evening, I was disheartened because I had reached a milestone. I had just turned 50 and had been diagnosed with physical illnesses that often come with reaching maturity in America: a high cholesterol level, hypertension and a hiatal hernia. I had also played two sets of tennis, that morning. My arms and legs were stiff and it was painful to walk up stairs or to stoop to pick something off the floor.

My husband, always sensitive to my moods, walked into the room, fondled my hair, and asked, "What's going on?" I replied, "Oh, nothing ... I'm just getting old."

* * *

Upon arrival at my parents' home, my father briskly walked over to me, gave me a quick hug, and took the suitcase with which I was struggling, out of my hands. He refused my offer to carry it myself tossing off one of his teasing remarks always said in loving humor, "You can't carry it. You're too weak." He smiled at me with twinkling eyes. I bristled at his comment. Still, although I reacted with over-sensitivity to this truism, I noticed that he managed the suitcase easily ... this 5 feet 6 inches, 135 pound, 87 year old, Chinese man.

I spent a lot of time with Dad, that weekend. We walked and chatted. I observed him with a new interest and asked a myriad of questions.

"Do you get a regular physical check up?"

"Yes. Through my health plan with Kaiser Health Care."

"How's your blood pressure?"

"My doctor always reports no problem. "

"Are you on any medications?"

"No. Your mother always tries to give me vitamins. Sometimes I take them to make her happy but most of the time I throw them away when she's not looking."

"When I used to live at home, I remember that you would visit Dr. Sia (a Western trained doctor) when you had a cold. Then you would get a tea mixture from the Chinese herbalist. Do you still do that?"

"Yes. To insure my health, I will use whatever makes sense from both Chinese and Western medicine."

I was quieter and more reflective, that weekend, listening to the older members of my family with an emerging respect. I sat with Aunty Mae, who talked about her daily, early morning walk to the park with a friend to participate in Taijiquan . . . and her weekly massage. While sharing a cup of tea with Uncle Ed, I was fascinated with his reflections of Western philosophies entwined with Taoist thought. I learned of meditation . . . of the benefits of quiet time . . .of centering within oneself. I noticed those of my generation with excess weight and protruding bellies. I watched my cousin Art gingerly nurse his back problem and Gary who groaned as he got up from sitting on the floor.

I took a second look at our elders. They were more physically fit than we. Slender and disease-free, they moved with ease and flexibility. The thought that plagued my mind, and that I finally acknowledged with reluctance was, "Is there a lesson to be learned here?"

* * *

When I finally made it to the last step of the stairs to our second-floor bedroom suite, I plopped down to catch my breath. Sitting there I realized that it was getting increasingly difficult to make it this far although I was bounding up these same stairs just a month before. I reflected on my physical reactions in the last month, shortness of breath, decreased stamina, chronic coughing, increased fatigue. Thinking that it was the beginning of a cold or, at worse --- influenza, I rested, ate lightly and drank liquids waiting for the illness to pass. However, the symptoms worsened so I made an appointment to see my internist.

As she examined me, she held her stethoscope to my heart for a longer time than usual. She finally said, "I'd like you to see a cardiologist." I asked if I should call his office for an appointment. She replied, "No. I'll call him. Go downstairs to his office right away."

I returned to cardiology three days later for results of testing that began on the day that I first saw my internist. The cardiologist was somber.

The diagnosis was cardiomyopathy, my heart was failing. I was informed that treatment would begin immediately, medications to attempt to assist my rapidly weakening heart and registration with a transplant facility to wait and see if a healthy heart would become available before mine completely gave out.

I called my husband at his office and we arrived at home at about the same time. We sat in stunned silence. I recovered from our initial disbelief and devastation before he did, he who didn't want to face the fact that my death could be imminent. With his assistance, I began to get my affairs in order, arranging for my patients to be transferred to a trusted colleague, updating my will and, most difficult for my husband, choosing a burial site.

Although my stamina began to increase somewhat with the help of the medications, I was still very weak and I slept off and on throughout the day. Between these resting periods, I sat next to a window in my study and looked through magazines and journals, seeking information regarding my disease and reading treatises about resolving and understanding the concept of death. In my readings, I came upon an article discussing partnering with your physician to facilitate physical improvement and possible cure. Certain techniques, if practiced regularly, would strengthen the body's immune and healing potential by reducing stress, putting the body's systems back in balance and increasing physical well-being. Along with the treatment of the physician, these activities would provide the very best physical environment for the possibility of cure.

As I read on, I realized that I had heard this before. However, it was not in terms of Western medicine. It was over a cup of tea at a family gathering. This was Qigong, the ancient Chinese way of healing.

* * *

I am thrilled to report that after a year of following my doctor's recommendations and partnering with him by doing specific immune-building activities, my heart began to function normally and my name was removed from the transplant list. It has been five years since my diagnosis. I continue to have bi-annual checkups and to heed the advice of my Western physician. I have visited Taoist temples, studied with healing masters and read translations of the ancient Chinese medical books to learn more about Qigong. I have also probed the minds of researchers and trained with teachers of Psychoneuroimmunology, the Western medical discipline that uses mind-body techniques to increase immunological resistance to illness and disease. I now use the best of both worlds to maintain my health and that of my patients. It is with pleasure and humility that I share this "Healing Force."

Contents

Part One The Healing Journey

Part Two The Way of Health

Part Three Paths to Recovery

Part Four Charting Your Personal Course

PART ONE

* * *

The Healing Journey

Chapter 1

Qigong
Ancient Chinese Medicine

Health is not an absence of illness ... it is a way of life.
- - - *Taoist Proverb*

In the soft light of early morning, when the gold of the day is gently replacing the blue haze of dawn, the parks throughout China are filled with people moving, swaying, stepping and bending to an inner rhythm. Like their forefathers did for thousands of years, they are seeking balance and harmony within themselves and with nature. They're practicing Taijiquan, an aspect of Qigong.

Acupuncture, acupressure, herbal medicines and Qigong are the four methods of healing in traditional Chinese medicine (TCM). The first three methods are performed and prescribed by doctors. The last, Qigong, is practiced by the patient. According to TCM practitioners, Qigong heals physical problems and diseases. If practiced regularly, it also maintains physical and mental health. It is used to this end by people in China and in Chinese communities throughout the world.

Principles of TCM as it is practiced today, are evidenced in Chinese history. Archeological explorations and discoveries of medical artifacts from the Shang Dynasty, circa 1000 B.C., include early types of acupuncture needles. Primitive records suggest observation of medical conditions by practitioners. After the 1st century A.D., treatises in books discussed the use of acupuncture and herbal concoctions to treat physical disorders and diseases.

As communication and travel between countries developed and expanded, scientists were exposed to the ideas of other nations. In the 20th century, Western thought began to influence Chinese medicine. When the Chinese government adopted the Communist ideology in the late 1940's, the medical community was an arena of healthy competition between TCM physicians and those trained in Western medicine. In the 1950's, the government recognized the value of both schools of thought and officially supported both Western and TCM practices.

The focus of this chapter is on Qigong. When considering traditional Chinese medicine, Western readers are asked to suspend their world view and look at human and cosmic life from a different perspective. The culture and its interpretation of universal existence decrees its philosophy. TCM practitioners initially developed their ideas through observations of the natural world. Doctrines of several philosophies, particularly Taoism, also influenced thought. A primary premise of the Taoist understanding of the world is that everything is interdependent and interactive. No one entity can stand or survive without the others. To understand Qigong, one must also be aware of another basic premise; the centric concept of Qi.

Qi: The Life Force

In different parts of the world, throughout history, there has been recognition of general life energy in the universe. The Polynesians refer to it as "mana;" the people of India as "prana" or "kundaline." In 18th century Europe, Mesmer theorized about "animal magnetism." The Chinese call this life force, "Qi."

According to ancient Chinese metaphysics, Qi is "configurational energy" which underlies all of the organization in the universe. This energy is in the heavens and on earth, in the air and in living things around us. It is within our bodies and is vital to all life.

Since Qi is all around us and in the air we breathe, the literal translation for the Chinese word for air or breath is "a mixture of gaseous elements and Qi." It is not simply the oxygen inhaled or the carbon dioxide exhaled. It is a complex energy substance that is fundamental to life itself.

A Qigong practitioner views the Qi that he summons up in exercises, as "inner" or "true" Qi. This energy is the activating force of human life and is essential to existence. The goal of Qigong is to keep this inner Qi circulating smoothly but forcefully throughout the body. A practitioner can develop the capability to use his own Qi to move the Qi of others. When he is able to do this, he earns the title of Qigong Master. This level of skill can only be achieved by persistent practice over a long period of time taking years of concentration and participation.

Qigong master, Quo Lin describes Qi. "Qi cannot be seen by eyes and cannot be grasped by hands. But, a Qigong master can realize something moving and promulgating in his body; something like electric current within him making some tingling feelings."

The prevailing theme of traditional Chinese medicine is balance, harmony and interactive influences between people, the earth and the heavens. Optimum physical and mental health predisposes reciprocally beneficial relationships between these three entities.

Qi is the primal matrix of creation from which springs the opposing yin and yang forces that give rise to substance and material form. Different forms of Qi are acknowledged as they pertain to health and well-being under varying circumstances.

Three General Types of Qi

There are three primary types of Qi. The sky or universe contains "Heaven Qi" (Tian Qi), the earth contains "Earth Qi" (Di Qi) and people have "Human Qi" (Ren Qi). Each of these energy fields must be in balance to maintain maximum efficiency. When an energy field is out of balance, it automatically adjusts to regain homeostasis.

Heaven Qi is the energy field of the celestial sphere. Its rebalancing tools include the wind, rain, storms, earthquakes, floods. When it brings any of these phenomena into play, it affects the balance of the other energy fields.

For example, a readjustment activity of the Heaven Qi will have an impact on the Earth Qi. If the Heaven Qi is rebalancing its energy using rain and there are areas of the earth receiving too much rain, rivers may overflow and flood the land. If there is too little rain plants will die.

According to Chinese thought, Earth Qi consists of fields of heat, energy and magnetism. These must also be in balance. If they are not, natural phenomena such as underground activities and shifts in the earth's platelets will be necessary to rebalance the fields. Plants will be healthy and affirming and nature will flourish as long as the Qi of the earth is balanced.

All living organisms whether they be people, animals or plants, have energy fields. When these organisms lose or are unable to maintain their equilibrium, they weaken, sicken and eventually die. Necessary for good health for everything in the heavens, on earth and within individual living things are balance, harmony and reciprocal interactions.

The cycles of nature are the rebalancing methods of Heaven Qi and Earth Qi. These forces influence Human Qi. Understanding this interactional connection allows us, as humans, to adjust ourselves, when necessary, to fit more smoothly into the natural cycles. A primary goal of Qigong is to help us maintain balance within ourselves and with the energy fields that surround us.

Basic Chinese Physiology

The Western view of the functioning body is different from the Chinese view. Westerners describe bones, muscles, nerves, skin, and cells. Practitioners of traditional Chinese medicine refer to the anatomy of the body in terms of the basic Essential Substances, the Organ Systems and the Meridians.

• The Essential Substances

TCM integrates mind and body functions in terms of Qi, Jing, Shen, Xue, and Jin-Ye.

Qi is energy necessary for life. It isn't visible to the human eye. The Western mind often finds it difficult to understand the concept of Qi. It is described as vital energy, life force, breath of life. Human Qi is within us and fuels our existence. This energy circulates through our bodies. To maintain optimum health, the circulation must be strong and smooth without obstruction. If there is an imbalance of Qi, we have an excess of positive Qi (Yang) or an excess of negative Qi (Yin). Imbalance is illness.

Dr. Yang Jwing-Ming, founder of Yang's Martial Arts Academy in Boston, uses this example: " Imagine that your body is a machine with Qi being the current that makes it run. When you pinch yourself you feel pain. Have you ever thought, 'How do I feel pain?' You might answer that it is because you have a nervous system in your body which perceives the pinch and sends the signal to the brain. However, there is more to it than that. The nervous system is material and if it didn't have energy circulating in it, it wouldn't function. Qi is the energy which makes the nervous system and the other parts of your body work. When you pinch your skin that area is stimulated and the Qi field is disturbed. Your brain is designed to sense this and other disturbances and to interpret the cause."

Human Qi is best described by its functioning. It sustains all movement whether voluntary or involuntary. It maintains the body's temperature at an optimum level for functioning. It protects the body when it is invaded by bacteria or foreign subjects that could cause illness. It assists in the transformation of food and air into other vital properties necessary for life. It assists in keeping organs, vessels and other internal components in proper alignment. It is the body's internal energy, similar to the electricity that passes through a machine to keep it running.

Human Qi originates from the conversion of Jing which we receive from our parents, from the food we eat and from the air we breathe. Qi which is converted from Original Jing is called Original Qi. It is Qi that is pure and superior in quality to other Qi. Qi that is taken in with food and air is often of lesser quality and can affect the balance of the body by making it too positive or too negative.

When you maintain the quality of the original Qi, you are able to use the total Qi resources to generate continuous energy. Qi is stored in the Lower Dan Tian in the abdominal region just below the navel.

Jing is often translated as essence. It is the origin and most refined part of all life. It is the original source of being and determines the nature and the characteristics of every living entity. Jing nurtures growth and development. It is responsible for developmental changes of people from their beginnings as fetuses to their conclusions in death. It is the root of life.

Original Jing (Yuan Jing) is inherited from one's parents. It is the root and seed. It is also the basis for physical and mental strength. If a person's parents were strong and healthy, the Jing they pass down to their offspring will be strong and healthy and will provide a solid foundation on which to grow. To stay healthy and to insure a long life, a person must maintain and nurture this Jing. The original Jing is contained in the kidneys. When you maintain these organs you will have sufficient Original Jing to supply your body for a lifetime. If a person's Jing is weak, he may be chronically ill and prone to infection and illness. Although a person cannot increase his Original Jing, Qigong training improves its quality by teaching a person to maintain and strengthen it. Jing contained in food and in air is also necessary for existence.

Shen is the force of life. It encompasses the mind and spirit. It refers to the human consciousness and includes senses, emotions and thoughts. It is the will; the driving force behind behavior and actions. It gives Jing definition and impacts and influences Qi. When Shen is strong and vigorous, the Qi is also strengthened. When Qi is strong, resistance to disease and disorders is at its most efficient level.

The root of Shen is Yi translated as the mind or the intention. When the mind is activated, there is an increased alertness. There is also increased ability to concentrate and focus attention. The spirit is then elevated to new heights.

Xue is translated as blood. However, its functions are more than the Western view of its purpose. According to TCM, the Xue nourishes, moistens and lubricates the body. It anchors and stabilizes the mind and vitalizes the Shen. It assists in transporting the Shen to various parts of the body. The Qi interacts with and propels the Xue through the entire anatomical system. In this way, the Shen is also dispersed throughout the body.

Jin-Ye refers to all of the bodily fluids other than Xue. These include mucus, perspiration, urine and other secretions such as gastric acid and bile. Its main functions are to nourish the body and keep it moist and supple. It is produced by the digestion of food. Certain forms of Jin-Ye help to invigorate and produce Xue.

•The Organ Systems

Like Westerners, the Chinese recognize organs as structures. However, the focus of medical discussions and treatment are more likely to concentrate on the functions of the structure and the role they play in relationship to the entire energy process of the body.

Zangfu is the Chinese word used to describe the series of Yin and Yang organ systems that are anatomically identified in traditional Chinese medicine. The organs classified as Zang are the Yin or solid organs. These are the lungs, kidneys, heart, spleen, liver and the pericardium. Chinese physicians identify them as deep in the body. Their functions include producing, regulating and acting as storage reservoirs for basic fluids and substances. In Chinese medicine today, the functions of the Zang organs are recognized similarly to Western thought. However, additional functions that are related to the Qi are attributed to each organ. Each organ is also linked to an emotion.

Zang organs are paired with and work in conjunction with Fu organs. Fu identifies the hollow Yang organs which are closer to the surface of the body and receive, sort, distribute and excrete body substances. These organs - the large and small intestines, gall bladder, bladder, stomach and San Jiao (Triple Burner) - are involved in the continuous process of movement and change.

The San Jiao is considered an organ in TCM because its process can be identified although there is no recognizable anatomical structure. It mediates the body's water metabolism maintaining the ambient temperature and helps move the Qi.

In addition to the Zang and the Fu organs are the extra Fu organs which include the brain, uterus, marrow, bone and blood vessels. The gall bladder is considered both a Fu and an extra Fu organ.

For our purposes, it suffices to know that the organ systems are important to the constant movement of the fundamental substances of the body. Its optimum functioning is also vital to the distribution of Qi.

•The Meridians

The human body has twelve major channels and eight vessels otherwise known as meridians. The invisible channels flow throughout the body and act as conduits in the vast system that transports the Essential Substances to the Organ Systems. The vessels are the reservoirs and monitor and control the Qi circulation and distribution.

When the Qi in the reservoirs is healthy, it flows into the channels and does its work efficiently. When healthy Qi in the channels is adversely affected by obstruction or stagnation, the body can no longer function optimally. Illness occurs.

The system of channels and vessels and their specific functions is complicated. As with Western physicians, it requires years of study and practice to become a doctor of traditional Chinese medicine. Knowledge of the body's Qi system is essential to the practice of acupuncture and acupressure. All the information needed for our purposes is that each channel has a specific function. When a person experiences a physical problem such as a migraine headache, the Qi in the particular channel that affects headaches is negatively affected.

The effectiveness of the body's Qi is also influenced by the mind and mood, the weather, the time of day and the amount and type of food intake. The strength of Qi also varies throughout the day in a cycle of ebb and flow. It differs from person to person. The eight reservoirs will regulate the flow of Qi and normalize it whenever it is out of synchronization in one or more of the twelve channels.

When a person becomes ill, his Qi level is either too positive (excessive; Yang) or too negative (deficient; Yin). To adjust the patient's Qi level, a TCM physician might use a prescription of herbs, acupuncture, acupressure and/or physical and mental techniques called Qigong.

Illness and Health According To Chinese Medicine

The Chinese have been studying nature for thousands of years. Information on the patterns and cycles of nature are recorded in the *I Ching* (Classic of Changes). This book is a Chinese almanac, providing formulas for calculating the dates of seasonal change, when it will snow and when a farmer should plow or harvest. Nature is always repeating itself in routine patterns and cycles. These repetitions are caused by the balancing of the Qi fields.

In their research of nature and of the Qi fields, Chinese scientists paid particular attention to the interrelationships of natural phenomena and humans. They found that the well-being of people was dependent on their ability to maintain the body's Qi circulation in harmony with nature's cycles. If they could keep these energy fields in balance, they could enjoy good physical and mental health.

•Philosophy Of Health Beliefs

The concepts of balance and harmony are central to the Chinese philosophy of living. A Taoist saying perforces, "There are no absolutes. What is, is also what is not. In white there is also black and in black there is also white."

This premise of the balancing, complementing and contradicting actions of life forces derives from the Chinese concept of the primary opposites of yin and yang that are integrated in the universal force and symbolized in the taiji diagram.

Good health is balance and harmony between polarities. For maintenance of health, the most important polarities to be balanced are yin - yang (male - female), piao-li (outer - inner), leng - ji (hot - cold) and hsu - shih (empty - full).

When Human Qi becomes unbalanced, the body is affected and becomes damaged. Disharmony between the body's Qi and the body's fluids, (e.g., blood) causes illness. Chinese physicians diagnose disease by exploring how and where the Qi is unbalanced. They evaluate the condition of the body's Qi and interpret the visible physical symptoms. Once the Qi imbalance is corrected and the Qi is returned to its normal level, the root cause of the illness has been removed.

•Methods For Adjusting Qi

To adjust a patient's Qi, the Chinese physician will use acupuncture, acupressure, herbal medicines and Qigong healing methods. However, the Chinese people are also encouraged to participate in their own health maintenance and recovery. To this end, Qigong exercises were created. The ancient practitioners discovered that with regular performance of these exercise techniques, people were able to strengthen their Human Qi and slow down the degeneration of their bodies, gaining not only good health but a longer life.

Understanding Qigong

Qigong is an ancient system of breathing. This breathing state is reached through "vital energy" mind control exercises. It can help prevent and cure diseases, increase strength, resist premature senility and insure long life. *The Emperor's Classic*, an ancient Chinese manual of medicine, calls it a method for "warding off disease and prolonging life."

Qigong is the collective name for many Chinese exercises that allow us to gain control over Qi - the life energy distributed through invisible channels also known as meridians, in our bodies. It is the maintenance of the balanced distribution of Qi that guarantees health and well being.

• Categories of Qigong

Qigong activities are divided into two categories. Wai Dan , the external elixir of life, strengthens the external workings of Qi in order to protect the body. Nei Dan regulates and refines the internal Qi to insure that the organ systems work efficiently.

Wai refers to the limbs, which are external as opposed to the torso which contains all the vital organs. Dan is the Chinese word for elixir. The purpose of Wai Dan Qigong activities is to strengthen the Qi in the arms and the legs. When the Qi potential reaches a level of sufficient concentration, the Qi will flow through the channels, clearing obstructions throughout the body and providing nourishment to the organ system. This is part of the reason a person who follows a regular exercise program or has a job that requires movement, is generally healthier than a person who is sedentary.

Internal is the English translation of Nei. Therefore Nei Dan refers to the internal elixir. This elixir is in the torso. Wai Dan is strengthened in the limbs. It then moves into the body. Nei Dan is reinforced and energized in the body and pulsates into the limbs. Training to move Nei Dan is more extensive and requires more study and concentration than Wai Dan Qigong exercises. Historically, methods of strengthening Nei Dan were more jealously guarded by the ancient scientists and masters than Wai Dan practices. Although it is important to preserve and strengthen both the internal and external elixirs, it is Nei Dan that is particularly associated with longevity and good health.

Classifications of Qigong
According To The Goal of A Particular Training

Practitioners use different training methods which depend on their goal. The four main goals are to maintain health, to manage illness, to develop martial skill and to attain enlightenment or "Buddhahood." All methods have cross purposes. Methods to develop martial skill not only increase combat ability but improve health. To achieve enlightenment one must be in good health and be able to cure illness.

•Qigong For Maintaining Health

In 6th century B.C. China, there were two major schools of scholarly thought. One was created by Confucius. The scholars who ascribed to his theories became the Confucians. Mencius enhanced and revised Confucius' theories. His followers became known as Ru Jia (Confucianists). Basic to the philosophy of Ru Jia are the concepts of loyalty, filial piety, humanity, kindness, trust, justice, harmony and peace. Many of the Chinese core beliefs can be traced to the teachings of Mencius.

The second major school of thought was called Dao Jia (Taoism), believed to be founded by Lao Tze. The book of discussions of morality, *Dao De Jing* (Morality Classic), is credited to Lao Tze. Before the Han dynasty, Taoism was considered a philosophical branch of scholarly thought. Traditional Taoism eventually became integrated with Buddhism as practiced in India and thus, began to become viewed by some as a religion.

Both theories contributed to Qigong with a primary emphasis on the maintenance of health and the prevention of disease. Good health requires a state of mental and physical serenity. This state is synonymous with a balanced and harmonious Qi. It allows the mind, body, spirit triad to function at its most efficient level with a minimal amount of stress. The proponents of both schools of thought contended that many illnesses were caused by mental and emotional excesses. According to the beliefs, illness was equated with disharmony.

Scientists suggested that an important vehicle to gaining a peaceful mind was meditation. In meditation, a concentration of the training is learning to rid the mind of thought allowing it to become clear and calm. In this ultimate calmness, the flow of thoughts and emotions decrease in intensity and rate. The meditator's mind reaches neutrality. This neutral state is one of ultimate calm and serenity in which the entire being, including the internal organs, are deeply relaxed. When the body is in this condition, Qi flows smoothly and strongly without obstruction.

According to a chapter in *The Emperor's Classic*, training for true Qi should be carried out in three respects: 1) to direct Qi by breathing, 2) to safeguard the spirit independently and 3) to unify the muscles and the flesh. Scientists explained this further as regulating the mind, body and breath. This is the focus of Qigong training. If these three entities are well regulated, Qi flows naturally and maintains the optimum condition for good health. This training is called Xiu Qi. The Chinese word, Xiu, means to regulate, to cultivate or to repair. It maintains the ultimate functionings of the body's systems.

Initially, the concentration of the medical literature was limited to the maintenance of health. The basic premise was to follow one's natural destiny and maintain physical and mental health during the natural course of life. After the Han dynasty, the Taoists asserted that one's destiny in terms of life expectancy could be changed. They believed that it was possible to strengthen the Qi and prolong life. Through an integration of improved nutrition, modern medical technology and the maintenance of a healthy Qi, this theory has become a proven reality.

•Qigong For Managing Illness

Historically, the Chinese have always held scholars and teachers in high regard. That was as true in ancient China as it is today. The old rulers so respected and admired scholars that they often adhered to their teachings without question. Consequently, the emerging occupation of physician was not as highly respected despite new discoveries of medical science and techniques that proved successful, particularly if some of their beliefs were in opposition to the prevailing scholarly thought. Contributing to the nonacceptance of the new medical practice was the abhorrence of the method of diagnosing illness by touching a person's body. Touching of another's body was considered a trait of lower classes in society who were unsophisticated, crude and lacking in etiquette mores.

Ancient Chinese medical scientists continued their covert research despite scholarly derision. They wanted to know if the Qi flow could be affected by various manipulations. Information that they obtained by their studies suggested that sitting quietly in meditation was vital to the maintenance of health but solely using this method would not cure sickness. They proposed that movement was also needed to stimulate the Qi.

Through observing patients they discovered that people who moved and exercised regularly were ill less often. Their bodies did not degenerate as quickly as the bodies of people who were sedentary.

It was also discovered that the body's Qi circulation changed with the seasons and that the body required help in maintaining balance during these periods. Readjustment was required for optimum functioning. Further study revealed that different organs had characteristic problems during particular seasons.

Another finding was that specific movements appeared to affect the Qi in precise organs. From this discovery, it was deduced that particular movements could be used to treat illnesses in those organs and to restore normal functioning in these areas, affecting cure. A different set of exercises was created to counterbalance seasonal Qi disorders.

All of these movements played a critical role in restoring harmony and balance to the contrasting and complementary qualities that included Yin and Yang, fast and slow, excess and deficient, hot and cold and external and internal. Recovery of physical and mental health is a restored balance of the essential substances, organ systems and the channels and this was possible through the movements which have been refined as and labeled as Qigong exercises.

These discoveries opened up a level of understanding of the body's energies that no other theoretical system did and resulted in medical procedures that provided physical, emotional and spiritual fluidity and balance. Qigong has become accepted as a unifying process that creates balance, strength, agility and flexibility. It builds strength in the limbs and the torso, develops good posture and balance, and clears Qi stagnation in the channels and in the collaterals. It has the ability to regulate the properties of the body to create a healthy Qi flow throughout all the internal Zangdu systems. It assures vitality and the ability to function appropriately through old age.

Acupuncture, acupressure and the use of medications concocted from herbs and other natural ingredients are another direct offspring of the attempts of early practitioners to move the Qi by manipulation. According to TCM theory, ongoing imbalance of Qi in a particular internal area of the body results in physical damage to the organ in that region. The affected organ will malfunction and begin to degenerate. The imbalance of Qi and the weakening of the organ's functioning capabilities are the early stages of illness and disease.

TCM physicians began experimenting with these methods to treat the patient if organ damage had occurred. If damage had not yet occurred and the problem was diagnosed as stagnation and imbalance of the Qi, exercises could be used to readjust the Qi's circulation and restore health. Modern physicians in Taiwan and mainland China, have found that exercise can often cure diseases such as ulcers, arthritis and colitis. Acupuncture, acupressure and herbal medicines along with special diets continue to be the main procedures used by current practitioners of traditional Chinese medicine.

There is an additional technique used by TCM physicians that is particularly difficult for Westerners to understand. This method is Qigong healing in which the practitioner guides his own Qi, emitted through acupuncture points of the body, to enhance the Qi flow in the patient. Because there is no physical contact, the physician's Qi must be extremely strong and healthy. It takes years of training and practice to perfect this method.

•Qigong For Martial Activity

The use of Qigong for martial activity can be traced to the Liang dynasty (502-557 A.D.) Its origin in martial arts is linked to the Indian monk, Bodhidharma, who, it is believed, taught the Zen boxing that developed into Kung Fu, to the monks of the Shaolin temple. The Shaolin monks who were using methods of Da Mo's *Muscle/Tendon Changing Classic*, to maintain their health, found that they could increased the power of their martial techniques by incorporating some of the same principles. As word of this phenomenon reached the community of those practicing martial arts, master practitioners began experimenting with movement and developing physical routines that would increase their strength and fighting ability.

This concentration spawned Taijiquan which eventually became recognized as an effective and powerful fighting system. It was based on the Taoist principles of perfect harmony between the body's Yin and Yang energies and had as a primary goal, the smooth, uninhibited flow of Qi. Its development as a martial art can be traced to the Taoist monk, Chang San Feng in the 14th century. The conventional mythology says that he dreamed about a fighting dance between a bird and a snake. When he awoke, he began developing a set of thirteen movements that he saw in his dream.

As acupuncture became better understood by the community of martial artists, practitioners learned that by attacking specific vital acupuncture cavities they could disrupt the opponent's flow of Qi and create conditions that could precipitate injury and even death. Fighting techniques were refined and required training in understanding the route and timing of the Qi circulation. Then the practitioner would, effectively, be able to strike the enemy in a precise area with the appropriate strength to reach the exact depth required to prevail.

Qigong martial arts practitioners train toward the goals of being effective as the attacker and being defensively successful in withstanding kicks and blows to their own bodies. To become offensively skilled, the external styles must be mastered. These techniques concentrate on strengthening the surge of Qi in the limbs using Wai Dan Qigong. In defensive maneuvers, Qi is guided to energize the skin and the muscles, enabling a person to withstand a blow without injury. Wai Dan Qigong, to train and strengthen the limbs, must be balanced by Nei Dan Qigong to generate the body. Nei Dan, which is training of the internal organs and muscles of the body, counteracts energy dispersion and provides balance.

Some martial arts practitioners developed techniques that were not used for fighting; they were used for the maintenance of health. This style is known as Wuji Qigong. Wuji is a state of neutrality. If a person can quiet his mind to the point of absence of thought and feeling, the stillness of Wuji is achieved. When this state is reached, the mind is centered and serene, the body is relaxed and the Qi is able to flow freely to obtain proper balance.

Qigong movements are devised to cultivate energy. They regulate the system and prevent disease by developing Qi strength. A strong Qi fosters a smooth, calm effort that is free of stress-related obstructions. It coordinates the body's systems and prevents disharmony. It fosters good health and builds strength, which are needed in both successful martial arts and in maintaining good health. Similar movements are used toward both ends.

The movement forms have changed over time. They have evolved mainly within the context of family lineages. Many different forms are practiced in China. The most common systems used in the West are Yang (both long and short forms), Wu, Chen, Sun and Wu Dang.

•Qigong For Spiritual Enlightenment

Qigong as explicated by the Taoists and Buddhists are the practices that generally come to mind when a Chinese person discusses spiritual enlightenment. The primary training goal is the attainment of enlightenment or Buddhahood as referred to by those of that faith. Attaining enlightenment is the ability to gain so much control over the flow of Qi that one can use this skill to elevate consciousness to another level. Then the spirit may be able to transcend normal human suffering, move out of the continuous cycle of reincarnation and enter into the realm of eternal peace.

According to this premise, all human suffering is caused by negative emotions and desires. If, at the time of a person's death, she is still bound to these emotions and desires, she will continue in the cycle and be reincarnated. While she is still living on earth she must train her spirit to reach a level that allows her to bypass reincarnation.

This goal is difficult to attain with the distractions of everyday life. That's why those who are trying to reach this level often leave society and seek the seclusion of uninhabited places such as the tops of mountains. Here they can better concentrate on the cultivation and training of the spirit.

Marrow/Brain Washing Qigong is the method usually practiced to strengthen the internal Qi in order to direct it into the forehead, where it is believed that the spirit resides. Specific methods are used to stimulate the spirit and enable it to survive the demise of the physical body.

For the last two thousand years, the three major religious schools of Qigong training - Tibetan Buddhists, Chinese Buddhists and the Taoists - have been practicing Qigong according to these principles. More recently, lay practitioners have been using this method, not to gain enlightenment, but to prolong and extend life.

Qigong Training Principles For Good Health and Cure

Qigong training has two main purposes. The first goal is to maintain the smooth flow of Qi through the channels of the body. The second is to keep the reservoirs filled with strong Qi potential. Qigong should be practiced systematically, beginning with a comfortable level of intensity and duration for each specific person, to allow the body to adjust to the increase of Qi potential and strength within his body. Training correctly is essential to increasing optimum health and body strength.

• Energy Sources

There are four sources that provide energy to the body: natural energy, food and air, thought processes and movement. Natural energy is produced by entities including the sun, the moon, the clouds and the earth's magnetic field. The body's Qi is affected by these sources of energy.

Food and air are vital to the maintenance of life. These are converted into Qi by biochemical process systems. The TCM term for these systems is a Chinese word that translates into Triple Burners.

The mind is vital to the production of energy. Before a person can perform an action, a conscious or subconscious thought must form. This thought leads the Qi to stimulate the body parts necessary to perform the desired behavior. The more intense the concentration, the stronger the flow of Qi. Muscles are best energized by smoothly flowing Qi that is strong and healthy. Therefore, the mind is considered most important in Qigong training.

Movement converts food into Qi and therefore provides energy. An example of using all the sources of energy is Taiji Qigong or Taijiquan. In Taijiquan, the mind and movement are the two major sources of energy. If a person practices outdoors he receives energy from the sun. If he meditates facing South in the evening, he aligns himself with the earth's magnetic field and reaps its benefits. It is also advantageous to practice in the mountains or near the ocean where the quality of the air is at its best. Additionally, one should take optimum advantage of the energy available in foods by eliminating those that are fat-laden and unhealthy.

• Training Concepts

In Chinese belief, there are three treasures of life: Jing (essence), Qi (internal energy) and Shen (spirit). Practitioners learn to preserve the Jing, strengthen and smooth the flow of Qi and to stimulate the Shen. To this end, a trainee learns to regulate his body, his mind, his breathing, his spirit and the flow of his Qi.

To regulate the body, one must find and maintain his "center" and "balance". He must learn to relax to maintain ideal conditions for the smooth flow of Qi. Regulating one's mind involves being able to keep the mind calm and serene so that judgment of situations can be objective and the control of the flow of Qi to selected areas can be achieved. Regulation of the mind is the key to success in Qigong.

To regulate breathing, one must learn to breathe in concert with the mind with both entities in synchronic collaboration. With proper breathing, the mind will quickly enter the state which allows for the control of the movement of Qi.

With the body, mind and breath in harmony, one can then control the Qi by sensing its distribution in the body and manipulating it for optimum performance. This process aids in maintaining health and slowing down aging.

These concepts are common to all forms of Qigong. They are also adhered to in the practice of Taijiquan. To reach a deep level of understanding and to penetrate the very essence of any Qigong practice the practitioner always keeps these training elements in mind and continually examines them for better understanding and experience.

The benefits of Qigong training are not in the forms alone. Understanding and sensing are basic to the entire training. The opportunities to train the mind are limitless. The deeper your understanding and your ability to sense your body's elements, the more effective your efforts will be. Your continual development will increase the power you have to keep your mind and body healthy and well-functioning far into the future.

Toward Unity

Questions abound
Fears
Suspicions

A disorienting exposure to
Diversity

Struggling through the confusion to reveal
Truth

Is my truth his?
Is his truth yours?

Can we come together with
Universality?

I can participate toward that goal
Even if I have yet to coalesce into
Wholeness.

Chapter 2

Psychoneuroimmunology
Modern Western Thought

"Some minds seem almost to create themselves ...and work their solitary but irresistible way through a thousand obstacles."
- - - Washington Irving

Let me guide you through a short exercise that will demonstrate the connection between the mind and the body. Take a deep breath, exhale . . . and come along with me.

> We're walking along a dirt road that winds through acres of citrus orchards. The path is smooth, worn down by the foot trod-dings of the many people who have worked on the surrounding farms. The sun is shining and is warm on our bodies. The breeze is lightly blowing. As we inhale deeply, we get a tangy whiff of citrus. A lemon tree beside the pathway, loaded with yellow fruit, catches your attention. You reach up, pick a lemon and impulsively bite into it. The juice flows over your tongue.

What happened as you were reading this? Did you taste the sourness of the lemon? Were your salivary glands activated as if you were biting into an actual lemon? Many of you will have triggered a physiological re-action (a burst of saliva) to a mental image. You weren't eating a real lemon but the physical reaction was identical to if you actually were.

Psychoneuroimmunology (PNI), a relatively new area of scientific concentration, is the study of this type of phenomenon: how the mind and body interact. However, PNI involves more than the mind and body. It adds the immune system to the equation and takes into consideration the interaction of these three components and how the condition of one affects the functioning ability of the others. In their work, scientists who conduct research in PNI have learned that chronic stress in any of these systems can adversely affect the other entities.

But first, before we discuss PNI, let's consider some medical history.

Since the time of the classical Greek philosophers, Western medical practitioners have supported the tradition of separating the mind and the body. They considered the mind one individual unit and the body another. They had separate functions and communicated only as necessary to do their own jobs efficiently. Weakness or strength in one did not affect the other.

In reality, the brain and the rest of the body cannot be separated from those less tangible entities called the mind or the soul. Everything about us is contained in or emanates from the same physical frame. Every body unit interacts with the others. All parts are interconnected. What affects one, affects the others. Yet, in their zeal to simplify research and to possessively carve out niches of personal expertise, philosophers, clergy, scientists, physicians and psychologists have - from the time of ancient Greece to the present - treated the mind and the body as if they maintained unrelated existences.

Mind & Body: Together . . . Apart

The mind and body weren't always viewed separately. Some early thinkers saw all body systems as integral parts of a whole, cooperating with each other to efficiently perform the tasks required of it. In the fourth century, B.C., Hippocrates described health as a harmonious balance of the mind, the body and the environment. Disease was due to disharmony of these elements. Hippocrates is recognized as the founder of Western medicine and is the originator of the Hippocratic Oath. His premise that nature is the healer of disease is an accepted axiom of medicine to this day.

In the second century, A.D., Galen, a Greek physician, noticed that melancholic women appeared to be particularly susceptible to breast cancer. Although he did not research and expand this thought, he was aware that mood and illnesses could be interactive. He felt that negative moods, in particular those that we identify today as depression and anxiety, were correlated with vulnerability to illness.

However, Plato and other Greek philosophers surmised that because breath ceased with death, the soul and, by extension, the mind, was not dependent on the body. Plato was the first person credited with hypothesizing that the soul was something that survived beyond the body. He separated diseases of the mind from those of the body and called mental illness "divine madness." Divine madness was bestowed by the gods and therefore could not be understood by studying the human body. It was a notion clothed in mystery. Humans were not privy to the reasoning behind the acts of the gods. Why specific people were chosen to be inflicted by this madness was beyond the comprehension of mere mortals. Plato is recognized as developer of the philosophy of the soul separate from the body.

Christianity had a major impact on society's belief of the body and soul separation. According to scholars of theology, the word soul is literally translated in the Bible as "living person". As Christianity evolved, the concept of soul acquired Plato's views. The soul was seen as an immaterial and immortal agency that was separate from the earthly body. It resided in the realm of the ethereal. The influence of the church became more pervasive with the conversion of the Roman Empire to Christianity. Its beliefs and practices became the accepted dogma throughout Europe and extended to much of the Western world. The medieval Popes Gregory VII and Innocent II were instrumental in spreading their word far and wide.

During the middle ages, Christianity became the major Western social and political force. The church's position that the body and soul were separate entities became society's view. This official position that the soul was separate from the body became the foundation for modern biological science. Christianity proposed that the human body was made in God's image. It would, therefore, be a spiritual defilement to study the body even after death. However, if the soul was really the spiritual essence, then a nonsacreligious way might be found to study the earthly vessel in which it was contained.

When religious leaders accepted the belief that the soul and the body were separate, it was possible to portray the body as nothing more than mechanical. It could be viewed as just a robotic collection of nuts and bolts. The Church made its domain of philosophical study, the soul, which would last forever. Included in the concept of soul was everything that is now attributed to the mind: will, the impulse to act, passion, pleasure, conscience, agony. Like being close to God, goodness, the meaning of life and the thoughts and feelings that comprise it, were relegated to the mystical rather than the material world and could only be interpreted by those who were members of the clergy. The body could then be consigned to worldly scientific investigation, separate from the spiritual and intangible soul. It could now be probed, explored and surgically examined.

The scientific medical community acquired an enormous amount of knowledge when they were no longer prohibited from studying the body. They learned the configurations of the various organs. They were able to see, first hand, the connecting passages and tissues. They began to understand how different parts interfaced with each other. The study of the mind remained the sacred dominion of religion, and eventually of philosophy. In the early eighteenth century, when psychology became a formal discipline, it was not a branch of medicine but of philosophy. Its focus was on the nonmaterial, the subjective and the mystical.

The gap between the science of the body and the study of the religion along with the philosophy of the mind widened sufficiently to allow the study of bodily afflictions by medical researchers. Only then was it politically viable to research possible treatments for bodily infirmities. These investigations and treatments had to remain clearly delineated from treatment for mental disorders.

As a result, when new methods were developed to treat biological disorders, no one even thought of taking the mind into consideration. Activities of the mind remained mystical and invisible. Explanations continued to be based in religion. Facts of bodily import became increasingly available to observation. The mind was left to the clergy and scholars of philosophy. To the scientific community, observable meant real. The unobservable was spiritual or mythical. The observed as real and the experiential as unreal became the popular scientific thought.

... And Then Together Again

During the Renaissance period, Thomas Sydenham, expanded Hippocrates' observations about the healing power of nature. He proposed that a person's internal adaptation to external forces was a major factor in sickness and in health. He asserted that there were interacting influences between people, nature and the environment.

In the 1800's, Claude Bernard, the French physiologist who studied the role of the pancreas in digestion, emphasized the influence of the "milieu interieur," or inner state, on health and disease. He expanded the idea of interacting influences by including the mind.

At the beginning of the twentieth century, Harvard physiologist Walter B. Cannon, introduced the idea of the "fight-or-flight" response describing the body's internal adaptive reaction to a threat. When confronted with danger, the body has an automatic response to protect itself in some way. It confronts the threat by standing its ground and going to battle or it escapes peril by running from it. In the process of this response, the body of a person or an animal who is under the threat of danger, secretes catecholamines that immediately arouse key organs. The most widely known of these hormones is epinephrine (adrenaline) which is produced by the adrenal glands.

The "fight-or-flight" response was extremely necessary to survival when human beings were faced with life-threatening events. A confrontation with wild animals or standing toe-to-toe with an adversary in battle could have dire consequences. This exigency triggered acute stress in people and could only be successfully dealt with by fighting or running away.

The stresses we face today are more likely to be psychological or interpersonal and are not always best handled by fighting or fleeing. Hans Selye, researching stress at McGill University in the 1950's, demonstrated that the body continues to react to today's stresses as though it is facing an actual physical threat. It continues to produce epinephrine in amounts sufficient to heighten alertness and vigilance. It prepares to respond quickly and with great speed or force.

• Physiology of Stress and Disease

Both acute (short-term) stress and chronic (long-term) stress affect the body's health. If a person is under chronic stress - continual pressure to increase production at work or ongoing marital problems - his body reacts the same way it would if under acute stress - a near miss on the freeway or a sudden fall down a flight of steps. Catecholamines trigger physiological responses that prepare the body to react: the heart rate increases, blood pressure rises, muscles tense, breathing becomes shallow and quick, the stomach and intestines become less active and the blood sugar rises for quick energy. These physical reactions are accompanied by a psychological response. The person may experience racing thoughts, a sharper focus of attention, anxiety and even panic.

This reaction is necessary in the event of a life-threatening mishap. If you are crossing a street and the driver doesn't see you and therefore, doesn't slow down or stop, you want to have quick enough reactions to jump out of the way and avoid getting hit. However, continual, unceasing production of epinephrine is detrimental to health. In that case, the body would maintain its stress reaction at such a heightened level that the immune system eventually wears down. This immune suppression leaves you at risk for illness.

In today's society, there are many things that are stressful. Some of us have work responsibilities. Relationships can be challenging. We worry about money. Do we have enough to meet everyday needs? Will we be able to live comfortably when we retire? We worry about our children's safety. Will something happen to them when they're out without us? As we get older, we worry about non-specific pain. Do my headaches indicate a debilitating illness? A brain tumor?

When we constantly obsess about these issues, the stress we experience is generated purely in our heads. "But, these are real possibilities," you may say.

Stress hardy people, those who always look content and seldom seem to be ill, handle problems differently than many of us do. They identify the problem and implement a solution. If there isn't an immediate solution, they devise a plan for the long term. They also realize that everything is not under their control and that there are many situations that they will have to accept as is.

If money is a concern, they evaluate their perceived requirements for life and adjust them to fit within their financial means. Most us of have more things than we need. Life would be simpler if we had less. Think of living in a home with less clutter! Stress hardy people plan for the future by saving a specific amount of money each month. They decide on that amount by meeting with a financial advisor. They make sound investments.

If they're concerned about health, they have checkups with their physician. They schedule them regularly. They follow their doctor's advice to remedy the problems. If they get a clean bill of health, they continue their health regimen of eating well, getting enough rest and exercising without worry, knowing that they are doing the best they can for themselves. They evaluate their health realistically and make appropriate decisions. If you have pain in your knees and you're 50 pounds overweight, it is irrational to demand knee surgery. The appropriate decision would be to re-evaluate your pain after you lose the extra 50 pounds. Stress hardy people are proactive in taking care of themselves.

The catecholamines produced during stress responses - including adrenaline and cortisol - can have profound effects on the body's systems. The immune, cardiovascular, digestive, endocrine and neurological systems are designed to withstand sporadic onslaughts of these chemicals. However, when these bursts of stress chemicals occur frequently and daily, changes within these systems begin to happen to allow the body to adapt to the chemicals. These adaptations can take the form of raised blood pressure, increased blood sugar levels and decreased immunity.

With chronic stress, the immune system becomes suppressed and less active. It leaves a person more susceptible to colds, influenza and to more serious illnesses. Blood cholesterol level rises and calcium is lost from bones. Blood pressure can become hypertension. Muscle tension can lead to severe headaches or aggravated pain. Changes in the activity of the intestinal tract can lead to diarrhea. Increased heart rate can lead to arrhythmia. If the pressure continues, the adaptation moves to long term, chronic status. This state can be followed by life-threatening illnesses or even death.

The diseases that we suffer today are ones that slowly develop over time. The effects accumulate and compound until we have cancer, heart disease, diabetes or cerebrovascular disorders. Long term stress can be a major factor in causing or exacerbating these types of diseases. Stress can also hamper cure. Stress-related illnesses develop, mainly because our stress response, which has evolved so that we can appropriately react to acute physical emergencies, is often activated in less immediate situations. We sometimes turn it on for months on end with constant, mind-generated worrying.

The way the body reacts to stress is primarily governed by the autonomic nervous system, a part of the nervous system over which we have no direct voluntary control. It has two branches: the sympathetic nervous system and the parasympathetic nervous system. The sympathetic nervous system regulates arousal. The parasympathetic nervous system controls a counteractive set of responses.

The parasympathetic nervous system induces relaxation to help the body compensate for sustained periods of high arousal. It performs this function by lowering the heart rate, muscle tension and blood pressure. These relaxation responses are biologically regenerating and help the body to recuperate and return to a balanced state. Relaxation responses are necessary to help the body return to equilibrium, the condition necessary to allow the body to strengthen its resources and prepare for the next time it needs to react quickly.

In this relaxed state, known as homeostasis, our bodies have an ideal level of oxygen, an ideal amount of acidity and an ideal temperature. To maintain us well, these and other body factors need to be kept at an optimum level for the current circumstances. Automatically taken into consideration, are entities such as the time of day, the season, the age of the organism. A stressor can be anything that throws us out of balance - injuries, illness, an unforeseen emergency. Stress management techniques, when practiced regularly, induce a positive parasympathetic state. A homeostatic balance is restored.

The Immune System

To better understand how the mind can affect health, it's important to have a basic knowledge of the immune system. The two major branches of this protective complex are the humoral and the cellular immune systems. White blood cells called B-lymphocytes, produce antibodies in the humoral system. Antibodies are proteins that are key to the body's defense against bacteria and viruses in body fluids.

The cellular immune response defends against cancer cells and other viruses that have invaded and taken up residence in the body's cells. Key to this cellular system are the white blood cells including leukocytes, lymphocytes (T - cells, B - cells, natural killer cells), and macrophages. Their function is to destroy and clear the body of foreign substances - and of cells that are infected by foreign substances - such as bacteria and viruses. To do this effectively, they must be able to discriminate between themselves and foreign entities and ignore other white blood cells.

The organs of the immune system are the bone marrow, the thymus, the lymph nodes and the spleen. White blood cells are manufactured in the bone marrow and are dispersed throughout the body. They develop, move out into other areas of the body and lie in wait for foreign substances in their designated areas. They congregate in the lymph vessels and the lymph nodes, the filtering system for the lymph. One set of lymphocytes (T-cells) develops in the thymus where they hone their ability to distinguish themselves from precursors. They are in the spleen, the filtering system for the blood. The gastrointestinal tract has Peyer's patches with a high density of white blood cells. They are in the tonsils of the respiratory tract and in the skin. They are also in waiting near the body's openings to the outside. Those are prepared to destroy any germs and other infectious agents that are trying to enter to cause havoc to our systems.

•The Immune Process

When foreign entities first enter the body they can often be destroyed or dispelled by bodily secretions or other mechanisms. Sneezing and coughing prevent invading organisms from entering by blocking them and flinging them out of our bodies. A type of mucous can block bactericidal substances' ability to adhere to cells. If bacteria is not destroyed, they then come in contact with the immune system in several ways. They can be carried via the bloodstream to the spleen. They can lodge in the tissues and then be transported into the lymphatic vessels and nodes. They can enter the gastrointestinal or respiratory tracts and lodge in their lymphoid organs.

Inflammation is a mechanism of the immune system's first line of defense. This is a complex set of events designed to bring immune cells into damaged areas so that they can destroy or inactivate foreign invaders and allow the body to repair damaged tissue. The process includes increased blood flow, increased vascular permeability, the flow of fluid into tissues, fever, the penetration of immune cells into the tissue, destruction of the invader and tissue repair.

The macrophages also arrive and engage by grabbing and ingesting the bacterial organisms. An interesting phenomenon is the display of a piece of the bactericidal substance (antigen) by the macrophage on it's surface as a signal to other cells that the body is infected. This is called antigen presentation. In this manner, the macrophages alert and activate the other cells and spur them to action.

The natural killer cells also engage to kill virally infected cells and produce interferon to enhance killing and inhibit viral reproduction. Also activated are plasma proteins that, when in a sequence, can punch holes in bacteria and render them less effective or helpless.

The immune system's second line of defense requires a fit between immune cells and a specific target. Each type of immune cell is designed to attack a particular antigen. Some attack virally infected cells, some attack cancer cells. Some attack transplanted tissues and organs that are not completely compatible with the body, much to the frustration of transplant surgeons and their patients.

Most of the action of the immune system takes place via communication substances called cytokines. These protein molecules act on receptors. Different molecules have different functions.

These functions include the activation of cytotoxic T cells, macrophages and natural killer cells. Another important function is the enhancement of the body's resistance to viruses.

• Effects of Stress

There is no one cause of a particular disease. We can't say that we did this and therefore we got that. It is impossible to identify, with assurance, the reasons one person gets a disease and another does not. Every disease is multifactorial. There are biological factors. Is there a family predisposition for a particular disease? There are environmental factors. Do you live in an area that has a large concentration of carcinogens in the air? There are behavioral factors. Do you make healthy behaviors such as eating healthy foods and exercising part of your daily routine? Do you refrain from smoking? There are psychological factors. Are you constantly negative, sad, angry, stressed? Or are you a happy, positive, upbeat person?

The information in this book particularly focuses on stress and the immune system. However, it's important to keep in mind that these other factors also influence our ability to keep ourselves immunologically strong.

When chronic stress and other factors suppress the immune system, the body becomes susceptible to diseases. Infections are conditions with which the average person is most familiar. Germs are all around us and some of them enter our bodies. The job of our immune system is to destroy or dispel them and it generally does so with efficiency. If it does not, we get sick. By strengthening and enhancing our immune system, it is possible to reduce the chance that foreign substances entering out bodies can harm us.

Western medicine has been skilled at developing weapons such as antibiotics to combat infectious bacteria. However, scientists have discovered that as antibacterial medicines have become stronger and more efficacious, so has bacteria. Like many organisms do, they evolve and adapt to insure their survival.

An increasing number of Western scientists are recognizing that the Eastern medical point of view may be more effective in maintaining our health. The primary goal of traditional Chinese medicine has always been, not to fight disease and illness already contracted, but to keep the body strong so that invading bacteria and viruses do no harm.

In some instances, Western doctors already use, as a treatment method, strengthening the affected organ instead of eliminating the cause. For example, there are hundreds of kinds of viruses that can make us ill. It's impossible to identify all of them much less develop substances to kill them. For virally-induced problems, the most effective solution known at this time is to strengthen the functionings of the organ. Maintaining a well-functioning immune system is essential to our good health and to our ability to recover.

A healthy immune system is important to keep our bodies operating at an optimum level. As you know by now, its job is to patrol the body and destroy any invading antigens that can make us sick. However, there are opportunistic diseases whose malignant cells take advantage of weakened systems and create havoc if not quickly held in check. Two examples are cancer and HIV / AIDS.

Cancer is a disease that takes advantage of long-term immune suppression. It presents a particularly difficult challenge because the course is, initially, slow and cumulative and often undetectable. However, the presence of cancer in the body, even in the earliest stages, represents significant failure of the immune system. By the time detection is made, the cancer cells are dividing at a very fast pace and are well into doing their damage of replacing healthy cells.

A cancer begins with a cell that has been incorrectly coded and therefore does not have the accurate genetic information to perform its intended function. Several factors would cause the cell to get incorrect information. It may have been exposed to harmful substances. It could have been imperfectly formed by the body in its process of constantly reproducing billions of cells.

If the immune system is weakened and it doesn't do its job of killing the imperfect cell, the cell may reproduce other cells with the incorrect genetic makeup. These defective cells then begin to mass to form a tumor. They continue to divide and as their numbers increase, their growth accelerates. As they rapidly multiply they begin to intrude on adjoining tissue. They block proper functioning of body organs by expanding to the point where they put pressure on those organs.

They may also replace enough healthy cells in an organ that the organ is no longer able to function.

Normal cells replace themselves at a given rate. They are connected to a cellular communication system that lets them know how many cells to produce to keep the body functioning well. Cancer cells are faultily formed and cannot interpret the information accurately. They don't get the correct messages so they reproduce with reckless abandon.

In later stages of the course of the disease, they may metastasize. At this stage, malignant cells break loose from the original mass and are transported to other parts of the body where they continue their reproduction cycle and form new tumors. The immune system is overwhelmed.

The work of some researchers studying the interactions of cancer and the immune system suggests that the immune system may play a larger role in controlling metastases. It may have less influence over control of the initiation of the tumor. This indicates a continued need to participate in activities that strengthen the immune potential if you have a diagnosis of cancer.

AIDS, Acquired Immune Deficiency Syndrome, is another disease that takes advantage of a weakened immune system. In this case, a virus, Human Immunodeficiency Virus (HIV), weakens the immune system. If this virus is strong enough to overcome the effects of the immune reaction, it attacks and destroys a person's immune system until this system is unable to fight off infection. This phase is called having HIV disease. AIDS is the life-threatening stage of HIV disease.

Earlier in this chapter under the section on the immune system, the category of cells called lymphocytes was mentioned. Within this diverse group are the T cells. T cells participate in immune responses in two primary ways: some direct and regulate immune system responses; others attack and destroy infected cells including those malignant with cancer. A subset is called T helper cells. They are regulators of the immune response. They signal the immune system when an antigen is present and activate other cells in the immune system.

HIV weakens and then disables the immune system by directly attacking the immune cells or indirectly, by killing the T helper cells and impeding the signaling process needed to stimulate an immune response. An immune system disabled by HIV can no longer fight off infections that are normally brought under control by a well functioning system. This leads to advanced immune deficiency and vulnerability to life threatening disorders.

It is well documented in the medical literature that there are conditions not considered immunologic diseases, that are also affected by stress. These diseases include cardiovascular disease, ulcers, colitis, arthritis and migraine headaches. Cardiovascular disease will be discussed in more detail because of its prevalence in the United States and its disabling consequences that can result in death. Additionally, it has been proven that we can do a lot to decrease our risk of getting this disease.

In the 20th and 21st century, the number one cause of death in the United States has been diseases of the cardiovascular system. Even though the rate of incidence has declined over the last 25 years, people still suffer from angina, heart attacks and strokes. There have been advances in technological resources including improved medications. However, scientists report that the greatest reason for the decline of incidence is primary prevention and a change of lifestyle to reduce cardiovascular risk factors.

These risk factors fall into three main categories: biological, behavioral and psychological. Each factor is strongly influenced by the presence of the other risk factors. All factors are synergistic; they are interconnected and effect each other. Having one or more of these risk variables increases a person's chance of developing cardiac disease. Conversely, having fewer of them decreases the possibility of illness. Major biological risk factors include hypertension, an elevated cholesterol level and obesity.

Hypertension is the consistent elevation of blood pressure. It creates strain on the arteries and contributes to the development of atherosclerosis, the buildup of plaque deposits in the arteries.

The heart functions in the following way. It contracts to pump blood out of its chambers and then relaxes and refills with blood. When it contracts, pressure is exerted against the artery walls. This force is called the blood pressure. Measuring blood pressure results in two numbers: the systolic pressure and the diastolic pressure. The systolic pressure measures the amount of pressure exerted by the heart as it contracts to force blood through the blood vessels to circulate throughout the body. Diastolic blood pressure is the amount of pressure in the arteries as the heart relaxes and fills with blood.

Under normal circumstances, blood pressure rises during physical exertion to respond to the need for more blood flow. Under psychological stress, the blood pressure increases as part of the fight-or-flight response. Repeated or prolonged exposure to stress may cause hypertension because of sustained high levels of pressure.

An elevated cholesterol level contributes to the development of plaque that can build up on the walls of the arteries. Cholesterol is a fat-like waxy substance produced by the liver. It is also found in certain foods. Carried through the blood stream, it is an important part of cellular membranes and particular hormones. It is also vital for the production of vitamin D. But, too much cholesterol in our bloodstreams can be a major risk factor for cardiovascular disease.

Obesity is described as being approximately 25% over your ideal weight. This can put you at risk for cardiovascular disease. In addition to the simple fact of the risk of being overweight, obesity can also contribute to the development of hypertension and high cholesterol levels.

Major behavioral risks include a sedentary lifestyle and smoking.

A sedentary lifestyle is one with little regular exercise. It is associated with an increased risk for cardiovascular disease. Exercising regularly helps to control weight, decrease blood pressure and reduce psychological stress. It doesn't take much effort to reduce your risk for cardiovascular disease. A short 15-minute walk five times a week will do wonders for the health of your heart.

Smoking is a major risk factor for developing cardiovascular disease. It doesn't matter how few cigarettes you smoke per day. Just one cigarette will affect your body in a number of ways. The carbon monoxide in cigarettes will interfere with your blood's ability to transport oxygen. This accelerates your heart rate and caused your blood pressure to rise. It can also interfere with your heart muscles' ability to pump effectively.

People who smoke are more likely to develop blood clots quicker than people who don't. This places them at a greater risk for strokes and heart attacks. If you smoke, the most important thing you can do to reduce your risk of cardiovascular disease is to stop. Your health begins to immediately improve no matter how much or how long you have smoked.

Some research studies done on women have shown that within three years after stopping smoking, their risk for developing cardiovascular disease was the same as for a non - smoker.

Stress is the major psychological risk for developing heart problems. It's described as the perception of a threat to either our physical or psychological well-being and the fear that we are unable to cope with that threat. It results in the fight-or-flight response. The research of medical scientists supports the premise that severe or sustained stress may increase atherosclerosis. Regular activities that reduce stress and foster serenity decrease our risk of contracting cardiovascular disease.

The Theory of Psychoneuroimmunology (PNI)

Researchers of PNI generally agree on the premise that psychological stress can suppress the immune system; that the effects can be great enough to increase the possibility of physical illness and that people who make relaxation, exercise and stress management part of their routine, can increase their immunological resistance to disease. These techniques, when practiced regularly, can keep the body fit and strengthen its ability to ward off illness. This is the best milieu for cure.

Chapter 3

The Meeting of Cultures

"Our true nationality is mankind."

- - - H. G. Wells

When the practices of traditional Chinese medicine with its herbs and acupuncture needles are compared to the treatment methods of Western medicine, the two appear to be worlds apart. Yet, if you think beyond the differences in the words used to label body systems and to describe the functioning of those systems, and beyond the healing techniques that may seem odd and unusual, you soon realize that the beliefs regarding good health and healing are more alike than different. You begin to understand that there are commonalties between the theories and practices of Qigong, rooted in 1st century B.C. China and of the 20th century Western discipline of Psychoneuroimmunology.

I'd like to take a moment here to digress a bit and discussed a basic principal of both cultures. Both Eastern and Western philosophies distinguish between two concepts: the concept of cure and the concept of healing. *Cure* refers to the recovery of health. It's what happens to our bodies when we come down with an illness or disease and then, through treatment or its natural course, it goes away and we are well again, free from that ailment.

Healing is more about the quality of life rather than the physical properties of the body. It's about good relationships, peace of mind, love, compassion, tranquillity. We can be healed and still be sick. However, healing can lead to cure.

Some Eastern philosophies affirm stratified planes of existence. After our bodies in their present form disintegrate, our spirit transcends to another plane of awareness. Those who are not healed cannot advance to the next level. Hurts, resentments, anger and psychic pain must be resolved before ascension is possible.

What ever our beliefs about the afterlife, there is a correlated principle that affects our present existence. As we let go of negative thoughts and feelings in our daily lives, as we heal our souls, our bodies' immune

---

properties are free to concentrate on cure. This release of toxic emotions is an important component of living a long and healthy life.

Commonalties Between Eastern and Western Health Beliefs

Both Eastern and Western medical practitioners agree that the body functions in ways that are specific to all living creatures. Every organism, including humans, has a natural recovery system. When we have an illness, injury, physical trauma or wound, our bodies immediately gather the forces of their recovery systems to attempt to bring us back to a state of wellness. This curing system works quickly and efficiently. In many instances, we don't have to do a thing but go about our business. The mending of a cut is an example that we've all experienced which demonstrates the body's curing capacity.

When you have a cut, the skin is punctured. The immune system immediately goes to work to repair the damage. Approximately a week after the initial wound you realize that it's almost unnoticeable. There may be remnants of a scab but soon the area is as good as it was before you were wounded. Restoration time depends on the severity of the cut and your state of health. If there are no complications, the cut mends itself without the necessity of treatment from a medical provider. The body has done its job of bringing itself back to the state of wellness. When we understand the following tenets, we have knowledge that will enable us to assist our bodies in returning to that state of wellness.

• Harmony and Balance

For thousands of years, the Chinese have been viewing good health as harmony within and between the mind, body and spirit. When the body is unwell, whether the problem be physical or psychological, it is in disharmony. The goal of a healthy way of life is to maintain and restore balance between all parts of the body. The body is constantly striving for balance, wholeness and wellness. This balance is the predication of good health. Conversely, when there is imbalance, there is illness.

Western scientists call this state of balance, homeostasis. As mentioned in the previous chapter, the body has ideal conditions that are required for keeping it functioning at an optimal level. Balance is concerned with, for example, the body's temperature, the degree of acidity, the level of oxygen, the age of the organism, the seasonal temperature outside the body. All of these factors interact and adjust accordingly. Our task is to keep the body strong so that it can easily shift to maintain equilibrium. Treatment to one entity should include consideration of the other components.

Western medicine has recently begun paying more attention to the interaction of all physical determinants. It acknowledges that the mind affects the body. When we're anxious our muscles tense. Depression leads to fatigue. Anxiety triggers shortness of breath and sweating palms. Contrarily, enthusiasm incites physical alertness. Excitement creates energy. Western practitioners also recognize that our bodies affect our minds. What we eat, if we are touched, whether we exercise, how we breathe influences our thoughts and our moods. As the Chinese have done for centuries, an increasing number of physicians practicing allopathic medicine are treating the mind and the body as a whole, instead of as separate units, in their prescriptions for cure.

An equally important universal goal is the balance of humans with nature. Because all living entities in the cosmos depend on each other for existence, collaboration is an advantage to all matter. Preservation and care for the natural resources in the environment promote survival, good health and longevity for all.

•Sensing and Awareness

To keep ourselves healthy and in perfect balance, we need to hone our abilities to be aware of our physical and mental sensations and to intuit our bodies' needs. It's important to be able to recognize what our bodies are telling us. In both Eastern and Western contemporary societies, there has been an increased emphasis on minimizing time. Everyone wants to get more things done in the period of a day. On our jobs, we work quickly to be more productive. We rush to squeeze as many appointments as we can into an allotted time-frame. At times, we even hurry through activities meant to be leisurely.

A few summers ago, when backpacking with my husband, he encouraged me to walk the trail at a faster pace so we could get to the campsite at a predetermined time. He was impatient when I didn't respond to his suggestion but followed my heart's desire to enjoy the trip in whatever form it presented itself. He was especially frustrated when I stopped, unbuckled my pack, sat on a flat boulder, removed my boots and dangled my feet in a cool, soothing stream.

When we rush, we don't give ourselves the opportunity to sense what is going on within. Practitioners of traditional Chinese medicine are able to feel the flow and stagnation of the Qi in a patient's body. They also teach patients to sense the flow of their own Qi, to monitor its functioning and to correct it as needed. If we pay attention to our bodies, we can become cognizant of what it needs to return to a healthy state. A common example is the feeling that comes from overeating. We sense the discomfort. Then we adjust our eating, not according to the usual time of our meals but by how we feel. We may even skip a meal to bring the body back to a comfortably balanced feeling state. Or, if we decide to eat the next meal, we eat smaller portions .

The predominance of people who are overweight in the United States is partially due to ignoring or not being aware of what our bodies are saying about our food needs. We tend to eat mechanically and without forethought. We often decide when we'll eat based on the time that we usually take our meals.

Pediatricians have often attempted to relieve the anxiety of mothers worried about finicky eaters by telling them not to be too concerned. Small children will eat what their bodies need. This is not to say that they will make daily choices of all the necessary nutrients but that over the week, their intake will generally consist of a balanced diet.

• Moderation

Both Western and Eastern practitioners advocate moderation in all we do. We can eat whatever we want if we do it with moderation. Moderation is important in all our pursuits. Activities in excess - exercising, sleeping, working - are detrimental to our physical and mental well-being. They can make us physically or psychologically ill. A marathon runner's immune potential is at its lowest point immediately after a race. Much of his physical resources have been depleted in the grueling exertion of sustained effort.

Along with daily responsibilities, activities of leisure that give us pleasure should be included in our choice of pursuits. The concept of pleasure has developed negative connotations over the years. It is the opposite of many of the principles that Americans inherited from their pilgrim forefathers. We have been taught that if we indulge in pleasure we are lazy and self-serving. We should be focusing on keeping busy, producing, achieving. We even use the word "work" to describe many of our efforts. We work at our relationships, we work at being a better tennis player. We ignore the fact that pleasure is a survival tool. Activities that are necessary for our survival and that of our species, are enjoyable. Think of the pleasure you get from eating, from taking part in movement activities such as dancing or athletics, from sex. Participation in pleasurable pastimes should be a daily intention. But these activities also need to be done in moderation. Doing things in moderation provides us with a healthy balance.

• Stress

Health professionals, universally, agree that chronic stress exacerbates disease. It can contribute to the disharmony of the body and block our ability to sense its needs. It can reduce the efficiency of the healing system by hampering metabolism. It can cause restricted breathing and contribute to poor circulation, impaired immunity defenses, toxic overload, obstructions of the mind and problems of the spirit. Balance in the immune system depends on our ability to manage stress and handle negative emotions in a healthy, life- affirming way.

When our stress level is lowered, our immune system is free to do its job of maintaining our bodies in a healthy condition and to rid us of illness-causing bacteria. It allows rational thought. We are also able to maintain clear minds that allow us to remember to make self-care techniques a regular part of our lifestyle regimen.

Anti-Healing Lifestyle Practices

Your choices in three major areas dictate whether you are providing your immune system with the best possible environment to do its work or whether you are making it difficult for it to go about its business of keeping you well and disease-free. Decisions in your daily living of what you eat, whether you exercise and how you reduce your stress level have a profound effect on your health.

Food is an example of a product that should simply provide our bodies with fuel. Yet we often use it inappropriately and in excess, much to the detriment of our physical and mental well-being. The longer we live, the more opportunities we have to cloud our judgment and to reduce our ability to naturally make our food choices in accordance to the needs of our bodies.

As we have modernized and advanced to the point that all our efforts are no longer for survival, we use food in different ways. We mask our anxieties and our depression by eating foods that we associate with comfort or reward. The foods we chose are often the ones that were provided by our mothers as treats. Cookies, candies and ice cream are popular foods given to children for jobs well done. As adults we dullen our receptors with sugar, caffeine, nicotine, alcohol and both prescription and street drugs. We then choose foods for the comfort or relief they provide us. We might also adopt a diet plan provided by a nutritional expert who follows strict one-size-fits-all dogma instead of considering our individuality and suggesting foods according to our specific needs.

As our lives become increasingly harried and we respond to the demands of more and more obligations, many of us, particularly women, don't take time to keep ourselves healthy. We have so many responsibilities and often feel that we don't have enough time in a day to meet them or to follow them through to a satisfactory conclusion. What tends to be sacrificed are the things that we have put on our "to do" list that are designed to take care of ourselves.

Activities such as going for a walk, sitting and listening to a favorite musical selection or participating in Taijiquan with friends, give way to doing the laundry, taking the kids to soccer practice or finishing a report that is due the following day. We disregard the fact that if we don't maintain our own health we soon won't have the energy or stamina to get through the day. We won't be able to fulfill our responsibilities or to do the fun things that we might want to do. Our bodies, like our cars, need continual maintenance and care to continue to function well. Many people take better care of their cars than they do of themselves.

Healthy Lifestyle Behaviors
Both Eastern and Western health professionals agree that the following self-care techniques are the most important variables in maintaining good health. These techniques focus on prevention of illness and disease. They are more effective than the use of medicines and herbs. They are more important to our well-being than treatment by medical providers.

• Nutrition
We influence who we are and what we are able to do by what we eat. Not only does our intake of food have an effect on what we look like but it is also fuel for all our body systems. Our choice is whether we provide our bodies with good fuel or if we clog up the systems and make our bodies work harder because they have to sort through all the gunk we've consumed to find the nutrients that they need. There are some simple steps you can take to insure that your body is well fueled.

Lessen your intake of animal protein. Eat less beef and pork and more fish, skinless chicken and protein from plant sources. Move to eventually eliminating all meat protein except fish from your diet. Increase your intake of plant protein. Eat whole grains which include oats, barley, millet, corn and brown rice. Make dried legumes such as peas, lentils, pinto beans, and chick peas part of your daily consumption. Enjoy nuts but in moderation because of their high caloric content. Eat more dark green vegetables such as broccoli, spinach, kale and collard greens. These vegetables are also a good source of protein.

Increase your intake of fiber. Excellent sources of fiber are broccoli, Brussels sprouts, cabbage and cauliflower. Another good source is bran which can be eaten in bran cereal and muffins. Fiber is necessary for keeping the digestive tract clean and well functioning.

Drink eight to ten glasses of pure water a day. This is in addition to anything else you may drink. Many people are chronically dehydrated. Drinking an adequate amount of water is essential to good health.

• Exercise
To maintaining a well-functioning body with all systems working efficiently you must keep it limber with full range of motion. This allows all body parts to perform optimally.

Include the following activities in your weekly routine and you will soon be amazed at how youthful you look and feel. You will also be able to participate in physical activities without pain and discomfort.

Keep your body moving. Exercise firms muscles, improves over-all strength and endurance, facilitates blood circulation, strengthens your heart and lungs, improves digestion, relieves constipation and reduces stress and anxiety. It will also boost immune potential and reduce your risk of developing cardiovascular and other diseases.

Do at least twenty minutes a day of an aerobic exercise and try to build up to 45 minutes a session. Brisk walking is an excellent activity which is inexpensive and effective. No training is necessary. We have all been walking for years. Swing your arms rhythmically to get a full body workout. Always begin with a ten-minute warm-up period, then do some light stretching. Follow your aerobic workout with a cool down period of five minutes of walking at a slower pace. To keep your workouts interesting, walk in different places. From my house, I can chose to hike a hill, walk around a small lake, walk through a neighborhood of big, old houses or stroll through a restorated downtown area with interesting architecture and charming restaurants. Here, I can stop for a refreshing drink under outdoor umbrellas. For added interest, alternate or substitute walking with other activities such as jogging, swimming, biking or rowing. Cross country skiing and snowshoeing during winter months are exhilarating and invigorating.

Weight train two to three times a week. This is necessary to maintain strength and strong bones for the rest of your life. Develop a routine that works both upper and lower body muscles and abdominals. Equipment can be as simple as hand weights that can be adjusted from one to five pounds and ankle weights that have the capability to allow you to increase weight as needed.

•Stress Reduction

As you now realize, chronic stress is a major cause of the weakening of the immune system which leaves the body susceptible to illness and disease. The remainder of this book is devoted to enjoyable activities that you can easily incorporate into your lifestyle to maintain your health, ward off disease and, if you are ill, assist your doctors in facilitating cure. Both Eastern and Western societies have stress reducing techniques that are unique to their particular culture. They also have activities in common designed to promote serenity and tranquillity.

Be joyful in whatever activities you choose. Worrying too much about trying to maintain rigid health habits can rob your life of vitality. Living optimistically with pleasure, enthusiasm and commitment enriches and lengthens life. Enjoy the moment. You will emerge renewed, rejuvenated and refreshed.

PART TWO

* * *

The Way of Health

Chapter 4

Staying Healthy Through Serenity

"Health is not a condition of matter, but of mind."
- - - Mary Baker Eddy

As members of modern societies, we are constantly bombarded by stress. There are work deadlines, family demands and gridlock traffic. Not only do we have daily responsibilities but oftentimes, throughout our day, we are accosted with unexpected surprises that require our immediate attention and focus of energy. Most of this can't be avoided. So when we are reminded that continual, unrelenting stress can exacerbate diseases such as high blood pressure, ulcers, colitis and arthritis, it is easy to feel depressed and discouraged.

However, recent findings are exciting and encouraging. Scientists have begun to acknowledge that the opposite of stress is serenity and that regular participation in activities that promote serenity can reverse the adverse affects of stress. Our abilities to withstand the onslaught of the hormones secreted by our bodies to help us in demanding situations, are strengthened. We are returned to a state of equilibrium. During activities that promote serenity our bodies rebuild and renew.

Good health is the condition of perfect balance with all systems of the body running smoothly. When a system is out of balance it strives to get back into that balanced state not only within itself but also with other systems. As we have seen in prior chapters, this desired state is called balance by Eastern medical practitioners and homeostasis by Western scientists. Serenity activities assist our bodies in returning to that state of perfect balance, the optimum condition for resistance to disease.

The goals of participating in serenity activities to reduce stress are twofold: to help yourself withstand short-lived stressful events and to diffuse the effects of chronic stress. The latter is a more serious threat because continual, sustained stress may not give your body the opportunity it needs to recover.

The quantity of scientific literature on the importance of stress reduction for health maintenance and recovery is exploding. It confirms that we can have a major effect on our health, well-being and longevity by the daily choices we make for ourselves.

Joshua M. Smyth, Ph.D. of North Dakota State University studied the effects of stress on asthma. He found that his subjects who wrote about an intense or traumatic event in their lives for twenty minutes a day over a period of three days, brought about an improvement in the condition of their lungs. A major factor toward improvement was the relieving of internal stress.

The stress reduction clinic of the University of Massachusetts Medical School in Worcester conducted a study with people with psoriasis. Thirty-seven people received ultra-violet light treatment. Nineteen people listened to meditation audiotapes. The first group's psoriatic skin patches cleared up in an average of ninety-five days. The second group who used just meditation as a relaxation technique took half the time to get better.

Andrew Weil, M.D. has found in his work that most digestive problems can be assumed to be rooted in stress. The mind has an unlimited capacity to interfere with the normal operation of the gastrointestinal system by disturbing the balance of the autonomic nerves that regulate it.

Serenity As A Healing Force

No matter what activities you use to attain serenity there are three criteria to insure that your chosen method is therapeutic.

To obtain the best results, be alone. An important aspect of the process is to be able to focus on yourself; to concentrate on what you're doing without unnecessary distractions. Some people are able to center within even when they're in public or with other people. Students in Taijiquan and yoga classes are taught to concentrate on their own movements while blocking out everyone else around them. If you're not readily able to do that, then the best decision is to be alone.

Centering is essential; staying in the moment. This state is called mindfulness by many Western advocates of mind/body medicine. If you find your mind wandering, immediately bring your focus back to just thinking about what you are doing at this time. For example, if you have chosen to sit in your backyard and commune with nature as your serenity activity, concentrate on the feel of the breeze, the sound of the birds, the fragrance of the flowers.

To get full benefit, spend at least twenty minutes in the activity. Twenty minutes a day, four to five days a week is a plan that would give your healing system regular opportunities to regroup. Every day would not only be ideal for your health but would give you a moment of extreme pleasure and joy in the midst of your busy schedule.

Following these suggestions will help you relax, breathe appropriately and allow your spirit to guide you to optimum health. Activities that you can use include meditation, movement, music and art. These and other pursuits are discussed in detail in Part II.

Chapter 5

The Serenity of Meditation

"One of the greatest sounds of them all ... is utter, complete silence."
- - - *Andre Kostelanetz*

Chuang-tsu, the ancient Chinese Taoist teacher, called meditation "mental fasting." Familiar to most of us is the concept of physical fasting, the withholding of all input of food to purify the body's essences. Mental fasting, in turn, is relieving the mind of all thought. It purifies the mind and restores the spirit's primal power by withholding all distracting thoughts and disturbing emotions.

In both physical and mental fasting, the cleansing and purifying processes are ongoing and automatic, but the precondition for triggering the process of self-renewal is the emptying of the body or the mind of all input for a regularly designated period of time.

There are different types of meditation practiced in both Western and Eastern cultures from the simple to the more complex. However, even the simplest meditation technique will promote serenity. Serenity fosters good health and provides a good healing environment.

According to traditional Chinese medicine, the reason for ill health and emotional distress is a lack of inner harmony. The bodies of all living things have a natural tendency to move toward harmony and balance. If we don't interfere with this natural tendency with chronic stress or physical excesses, the properties of our bodies' systems will ebb and flow to keep us in balance. When we find ourselves in the middle of stressful situations, conflict, or concerns that interfere with our ability to continue on a harmonious path, we are no longer in balance within ourselves and with the universal forces. If this condition is on-going, we get sick. Keeping the mind clear and calm is linked to the well-being of the entire body.

Both Eastern and Western practitioners agree that the relaxation of the whole body, the evenness of breathing and the emergence of the meditative state has beneficial effects for all of us.

When we are in this state, our bodies under go physiological changes. We develop clear minds, emotional ease, uplifted spirits and a sense of tranquillity. This is the state that is the best condition for the maintenance and the recovery of health.

One of the Taoist objectives in life is longevity in good health. According to Taoist teachings, meditation improves health, increases mental alertness and extends longevity. It assists in harnessing internal energy and distributing it to all parts of the body using breathing and concentration. In the moving meditation technique of Taijiquan, movement is added. Movements are made in unison with breathing and concentration to strengthen all the components of the self: the mind, the body and the spirit.

Basic Meditation Principles

There are some core principles of meditation. In Eastern thought, the over-attention to thinking is seen as a major obstacle to obtaining serenity because it takes us away from the here-and-now. It transports us into the past, into the future and into the hypothetical unknown - all areas that have nothing to do with the present moment. It is impossible to stop thought from occurring but it is possible to disengage attention from the interfering thoughts that do enter our minds.

Mental activity is normal. However, the goal of meditation is to quiet mental activity and achieve a mental state of stillness; a place free from fear, anxiety, apprehension and insecurity. We are then able to experience the underlying self; to find identity, peace and serenity.

Quieting the mind isn't easy for the average person. Most of us are constantly participating in everyday life. We're incessantly involved in physical and mental activities. We're thinking, planning, worrying and then trying to put our plans into action. But, to what end? Granted, there are some plans to be made and things to do to insure survival and comfort for ourselves and our families but beyond that what are we striving for? "Happiness," responds a majority of people when asked this question. The perception that happiness is found "out there" in our achievements and acquisitions is so strong in the belief system of so many of us, that it is often difficult for us to interrupt our striving to clear our thoughts and still our minds even for a minute.

However, one of the keys to good health is for the mind, which dwells in the body and directs it, to come into harmony with the laws of nature which govern all living things. Learning to comply with the natural way of things leads us to balance and harmony within ourselves and with all entities. When we clear our minds of thought, the mind is able to act in a natural and efficient manner. With enough dedicated practice, we may even be able to achieve that higher level of transcendence where our minds and bodies are in perfect synchronization with the life forces of nature. In this state of ultimate awareness, we are transported to a higher sensory plane which is conducive to physical and mental healing.

Meditation is letting go and allowing the mind to return to its natural state on its own accord. It helps stabilize the mind to achieve a serene state. It quiets the mind to allow us to connect with our spiritual nature. We are in a state of non-action. Non-action does not infer no action at all. It refers to the non-action of things that are contrary to the natural way.

During meditation, our minds shift to the direct mode of experiencing. We are in the moment. We experience directly instead of characterizing through language. We are unencumbered by self-blame. We have no thoughts of the past or the future. We are unhampered by opinions, biases and prejudices. We are being mindful; present in the moment. In this state, things reveal themselves more vividly.

Meditation techniques aim at changing attention. They facilitate our ability to shift away from the world of activity and turn our attention to a place of tranquillity. They allow the mind to sink into the silence of pure consciousness that encourages us to separate ourselves from outer stimulation. We can then experience the peace within.

Taoist meditation tells us to be one with our bodies, to make them supple so that Qi can flow smoothly and pulsate with vigor. In moving meditation we would also be able to stimulate and direct it to flow to needed areas.

• Breathing

Vital to effective meditation and to the health of the body itself, is breathing appropriately. The way we breathe is directly affected by our emotions. When we are angry or anxious, we breathe in short breaths. If we are sad or depressed we inhale with stronger breaths and exhale with weaker ones. Therapeutic breaths, which are natural when we are calm, are slow, deep and uniform. Inhalation equals exhalation. This kind of breathing calms the mind and keeps it clear. It fills the lungs to provide the brain and body with life-affirming oxygen and results in a relaxed state.

Breathing directly controls the autonomic nervous system. This function of breathing is the basis for almost every type of meditation, Taijiquan and Yoga practice. Our lungs control breath and energy. The act of breathing also regulates the autonomic nervous system. This combination forms a direct bridge between mind and body and facilitates balance of the bodily systems.

There are hierarchial stages of the meditative state. The level reached is determined by the amount of time spent participating. For maximum benefit, you must allot a set amount of time to practicing meditation on a regular basis. The meditative state becomes deeper with the passage of time both in duration and in frequency.

The goal in the initial stage is to achieve a level head, a harmonious disposition, a peaceful mood, a concentration of the spirit, and steady attention. There should be a decrease in distracting thoughts. If you are at this stage of your meditation practice, you may need assistance in staying focused and on not being distracted by interfering reflections. You can concentrate on the movement of your breath. You could also use a mantra; a word or sound that you repeat over and over again. if you choose to use a mantra, keep your focus on the word. Meditators in India often use words that provide a harmonic vibration; a word such as "ohm." The end of the word would be drawn out causing the vibration. Think "ohm-m-m." The vibration of the mantra connects you more deeply to the natural vibrations of your body.

When this stage is mastered, the mind moves to the next stage. It quiets down further and there is a subjective impression of only one continuous compact stream of awareness. The mind and spirit are peaceful; attention is focused on awareness.

During the third stage of the meditative state, there is a feeling of imperturbability and nothingness; an experience of stillness like a pool of water at rest or a sense of drifting along like wisps of clear smoke, riding on clouds.

When you come out of a meditative state, you return to active life with a taste of the inner truth of peace and serenity. You are slightly less attached to the materiality of the world. You are more able to bring mental clarity, peace and tranquillity into your every day existence.

However, no single moment of transcendence is likely to enlighten us forever. Our conditioning is so deep that it's not long before we are again caught up in the reality of the responsibilities of daily living. But a little of the meditative experience remains and our attachment to the world may not be as strong as it was before. After another period of meditation, it is likely to be even less strong.

Regular meditation is, therefore, necessary to remind ourselves of the glorious feelings obtained in the meditative state; the absolution of peace and serenity. As we give ourselves up to this state on a regular basis, we provide the ideal condition for the healing of our minds and of our bodies.

•Meditation For Health and Healing

Simply stated, meditating is sitting still, doing nothing and turning our attention inward. According to traditional Chinese medicine, energy follows wherever the spirit leads. By focusing within, our spirit enters our bodies. Energy follows this focus. It condenses and circulates healing the body, energizing the brain, balancing the flow of the vital energies of the systems and the organs, and enhancing the powers of the temporal mind as well as that of the spirit.

Practiced daily, it replenishes our essence which is necessary for life itself. It keeps the energy flowing and pulsating. It rejuvenates our minds with spiritual vitality.

Jean's Story

Jean is a 32-year-old woman. She is married and has two children, ages 4 and 1 and a half years. She also works part-time as a real estate agent. Until recently, she had no problems handling the responsibilities of maintaining her household, running errands and working. On the days that she went to her job, her mother came over to care for the children. She enjoyed the rush of juggling activities and found a life with such diversity, fun and stimulating.

But lately, she began feeling unusually tired. She and her husband enjoyed relaxing by watching television for a couple of hours after the children were in bed. When she regularly began falling asleep during her favorite television show, she made an appointment to see her doctor. After a complete physical, her physician informed Jean that he could find nothing wrong, that all tests were negative.

After spending some time asking her about her lifestyle and her daily schedule he concluded that she was close to burnout. She continually depleted her physical resources without replenishing them.

He prescribed a simple meditation routine to help her rest and renew. He suggested that she not watch television for six weeks. She was to go to a quiet room and begin relaxing her mind and her body. She could listen to some soft, non-vocal music and take a warm bath. When she was ready, she was to light a fragrant candle and meditate for 30 minutes. He recommended that she do this every evening for six weeks.

She followed his suggestions. At first it was difficult for her to allow herself to take the time for herself. It felt indulgent. She was depriving her husband of her company. There were always evening chores to do; she had been doing the laundry during commercials while watching television. But, in the back of her mind, she heard her doctor's voice telling her that it was vital for her health.

At the end of six weeks, she noticed that she had renewed vitality. She seemed to be re-energized. Her mind was calmer. Her emotions were stable and balanced. She felt great. She continued her meditation routine after the six-week period ended and still maintains the energy and the vigor to participate in all the activities she previously enjoyed.

The literature on Chinese medicine reveals meditation as the prescribed treatment for a number of ailments. Some of them are conditions for which Western medicine does not recognize a cure. Dementia is one of those afflictions.

In traditional Chinese medicine (TCM) texts, you can find discussions of forgetfulness and absentmindedness in the elderly. Western medicine reports one of the causes as the decline of secretions of vital neurochemicals. TCM calls this condition "brain essence empty" and "absent heartedness." Along with the brain depleted of essence, the spirit is also weakened by chronic stress cause by incessant worrying and external distractions. The spirit then loses control of energy. The energy leaks out instead of circulating internally because of sensory attention to external stimuli. Insufficient cerebral energy causes a decrease in the production and circulation of brain essences - hormones, neurotransmitters and blood, in the language of Western medicine - which in turn, impairs cerebral functions including memory.

Since energy forms the connection between body and mind, when cerebral energy is depleted and not replaced, the connection collapses and "the mind roams aimlessly without guidance."

Practitioners of TCM prescribe meditation to treat this condition. They propone that meditation can stimulate the production and circulation of brain essence, enhance cerebral energy and strengthen the spirit. This results in improved mental functioning. If meditation is regularly practiced before the onset of dementia, this decline of mental facility commonly associated with aging can be prevented.

Self-Hypnosis and Imagery

In Western complementary medicine, self-hypnosis is often recommended to reduce anxiety and decrease stress. Self-hypnosis is the ability to alter one's level of awareness and attain a more tranquil and relaxed state. This ability to change one's awareness is synonymous with the beginning stages of meditation; at the place where consciousness shifts and we become more relaxed as if drifting in a suspended state; one in which we are comfortable, calm and without care.

Using imagery is a form of self-hypnosis but unlike classical meditation, the practitioner uses thoughts to alter his state of consciousness. Imagery involves creating a tranquil scene that can be imaged anytime you want to slip into a relaxed mode. You can create the visualization yourself by just using your imagination. You could also have another person, a friend or therapist, help you by talking you through the scenario.

Imagery is personalized to each specific user. However, there are two important guidelines to increase effectiveness. All imagery begins with taking three slow, deep breaths to clear the mind and to relax the body. The second guideline involves time. The duration of the imagery should be at least twenty minutes for maximum benefit. You will emerge relaxed, refreshed and renewed.

Allopathic medical providers often suggest imagery for patients to induce a positive state of mind and to reduce pain. A visualization technique for cancer, adapted from Taoist internal alchemy, is used by patients in China, Tibet and India to assist in their healing. The patient is told to visualize healing energies flowing into affected organs and dissolving tumors and malignant cells. He then envisions the healing energies repairing damaged tissue, leaving it renewed and cancer-free.

Fred's Story

Fred is a 67-year-old retired tool salesman who lives in a suburb of Los Angeles. He has worked hard all of his adult life, making enough money so that his wife could stay home and raise their four children. His children are now self-sufficient adults. He has been successful in his endeavors and was now able to enjoy a leisurely retirement with his wife of forty years. He enjoyed playing golf twice a week, going out to lunch with his wife, and gardening. They took trips several times a year and were making plans for an Alaskan cruise. He laughingly said, "My only vice is smoking but after enjoying cigarettes for so long now, I'm not about to give them up." He had been smoking since his late teens.

In October, just before the flu season, he went to his medical facility for an influenza immunization as his internist has recommended that he do each year. These injections had served him well; he hadn't contracted influenza since he began getting the shots. So, he was surprised when he began getting flu-like symptoms - coughing, fatigue. He assumed that it was a cold which would eventually run its course.

But when his voice took on a raspy quality and the level of his fatigue increased he returned to his doctor. His internist recommended a battery of tests by various specialists. The findings confirmed esophageal cancer.

After the initial shock of the diagnosis, he began radiation treatments followed by surgery. He complied with his doctors recommendations and faithfully followed his medication and treatment regimens. He also began looking for information about the disease and started reading articles on the research of new and innovative methods of treatment.

When in his doctor's office, one day, for a follow-up appointment, he noticed some pamphlets in a display rack. One brochure advertised a conference for complementary medicine in Riverside, a city 45 miles inland. At the conference, he met a fellow cancer patient whose disease had been in remission for three years. They discussed their experiences with the illness. Both she and Fred were familiar with earlier video games in which Pac-Man "ate" the enemy. She told him about a visualization she used to assist her body in its healing. During her treatments, she would envision Pac-Man eating her cancer cells. Now that she was in remission she continued to use this visualization. As she laid in bed at night waiting to fall asleep, she visualized Pac-Man roaming throughout her body looking for cancer cells to swallow and destroy. She felt that Pac-Man was helping clear her body of malignant cells and keeping her well.

Fred has since incorporated similar imagery into his healing .

Techniques of Meditation

Activities in which the mind is keenly attuned to the inner natural processes - breathing, muscle relaxation and the circulation of Qi - lead to meditative states by subduing emotions, expectations, preconceptions, comparisons and characterizations. These activities shift awareness from everyday cares and worries that interfere with the ability to be serene, to an awareness of inner and outer natural sensations.

Choose one of the three techniques that follow. Prepare for your meditation experience by simply being quiet for a few minutes. Some people can center within and transport themselves to a peaceful mind state wherever they are. They can even be on a crowded subway train. However, for most of us, solitude is more conducive to effective meditation. Find a quiet spot: an empty room near a window that opens to a tranquil, outdoor setting. Make sure the temperature is comfortable for you. Wear loose clothing. If music helps you to block out thoughts, choose something without lyrics that is soft and calming.

Sit comfortably. A half-lotus position or sitting on the floor with legs crossed works for many people. If you don't find a cross-legged position relaxing, you could sit in a straight - backed chair. You may want to lie on a firm bed or on a mat on the floor. Don't eat heavy foods or drink alcohol before meditating. Wait at least a half an hour to let food digest. Let go of disturbing thoughts. Then begin.

Take three deep breaths. Breathe slowly. With each breath, clear your mind of thoughts and concentrate on the sensations of your body. Notice muscles that are tense and relax these muscles. Pay attention to the different parts of your body and relax them. Start with your head and facial muscles. Then your shoulders, your back muscles, your upper arms, your lower arms, your hands and fingers. Move to your chest, your abdomen, your pelvic area. Move your focus to your upper thighs. Let go of any tension there. Move to your knees, your lower thighs, your calves, your ankles and your feet. Continue to take deep, healing breaths.

Now that you are completely relaxed begin one of the following meditations.

Meditation 1 Simply experience the ordinary. Sit or lie and pay attention to the ordinary aspects of existence: the rising and falling of each breath; the colors and patterns seen through closed eyes; the weightlessness of each body part. Continue this for fifteen to thirty minutes.

If you have a tranquil outdoor spot it would be ideal for experiencing the most ordinary sounds and smells of nature. Close your eyes. Empty your mind of all thoughts and just pay attention to sensing. Hear the chirping of the birds; the gentle whooshing of wind blowing; the humming of insects. Smell the fragrance of flowers; the pungency of newly turned soil; the cleanliness of freshly sprinkled paths after a spring rain. Feel the gentle rays of the morning sun on your skin; the light, warm breeze.

Strive to meditate for the allotted ideal time period. Occasionally, you may not be able to devote fifteen to thirty minutes to this activity but don't forego it completely. Even five minutes will have healing benefits.

Meditation 2 According to Chinese belief, the house of your Qi, the energy source, is approximately two inches below your navel. Visualize your Qi in its house. Envision it as a small round sphere, the size of a ping-pong ball. It is comfortably warm and glows like a soft light. As you breathe, slowly move your Qi through your body and up to the center of your forehead. Then, at the same pace, return it to its house below your navel. Throughout the entire meditation session, focus on your Qi. Watch it move through your body. If you're distracted by other thoughts, refocus your attention and concentrate on moving your Qi. Repeat this sequence for the designated amount of time. Twenty to thirty minutes is ideal.

Meditation 3 This technique of mingling your essence with that of the universe is one that is often used when a person has an illness or disease. Sit outdoors or in front of a window. Keep your feet on the ground. Breath normally until you are relaxed. Then take three deep healing breaths. When you inhale envision energy from the skies entering your body from the top of your head. At the same time, allow energy from the ground to penetrate the bottoms of your feet. Allow the energy from both sources to meet in your heart and swirl around mingling together. Then exhale, and allow the co-mingled essences to disperse throughout your body, picking up the traces of disease and sickness and taking them out of your system through your skin and into the air. There it will dissipate and be cleansed by the universal forces. In this purified state, it is available for other living things to use for growth and maintenance of life. Keep your mind on drawing the renewing energies of the universe into your body and expelling your essence which carries your illness, into the air. Do this for twenty minutes. I set a timer so that I won't be interrupted by thoughts of wondering how long I've been meditating.

After your meditation, no matter which technique you chose, you will feel relaxed and refreshed. Your muscles will be pliant and supple. You will feel strong and invigorated. With daily meditation, you'll be better able to physically and mentally handle the responsibilities and the challenges that arise. You will face the rest of the day with a clear mind and an energized body.

Chapter 6

The Serenity of Music

"Such sweet compulsion doth in music lie.."

- - - John Milton

The universe is a tonal harmony of many different sounds melded together to form a whole. It is many entities vibrating and interacting as they fill the great silent space. Music and rhythms echo the eternal harmonies of the universe. These harmonies are powerful waves of life energy. They are the unfathomable source of all good. If we surrender to the rhythm and move with its pulse, it heals our souls and strengthens our bodies.

Ancient tribes throughout history understood the healing power of sound. Initially, healing practitioners used rocks clapped together in conjunction with the sounds of their own voices to manipulate the pulse and rhythms of a person who was ill. They believed that evil entities were working with the person's body and keeping its rhythms out of synchronization with the rhythms of the universe thus causing discomfort and pain.

People were not only treated individually, they were also treated communally. Tribal leaders organized healing circles where everyone came together to participate in their own wellness and to assist those who were ill. They chanted and drummed throughout the night. Some of them reached the level of healing trances. In these trances, healing could occur. Healers might also have visions that suggested cause of a patient's ailment and appropriate treatment.

Sound is an integral entity in every spiritual and mystical believe system whether it is a defunct practice or one that continues on today. More prayers are sung than spoken. The use of methods and devices for spiritual awakening - chants, sacred hymns, bells, drums - evokes a phenomenon of the mind and the body that has real consequences for total health.

Ancient Healing Practices

An indigenous healing practice that demonstrates the power of sound in the recovery of health is Shamanism. Andrew Weil, a Western trained physician and renown scholar in natural healing, calls shamans master psychotherapists who know intuitively and by their training how to take projected belief and turn it back to patients in the service of healing. Shamans are mediators between the natural and the spiritual worlds. This belief system began 20,000 to 50,000 years ago and has been practiced throughout the world in diverse places including Siberia, South America and North America. It has been the primary historical physical and spiritual healing belief of the American and Canadian Indians.

Shamans used steady, repetitive sounds to induce an altered state of consciousness in themselves and in their patients. This enabled them to join together to take a mental journey that would lead them back to health. Stones, drums and rattles along with chants and songs were used to produce steady, hypnotic rhythms. The steady, monotonous beat of the drum or other instrument used acted as a carrier wave. It helped the shaman to enter the level of altered consciousness and then sustained him in that state.

In the 1960's, Andrew Neher, a researcher in the effects of sound on the body, discovered that steady rhythm altered the brain activity in many sensory and motor areas not popularly believed to be affected by external variables. He found that numerous pathways in the brain are stimulated to produce an expanded state of consciousness.

In Shamanism, an essential ingredient was mutual trust. The patient had to have faith in the shaman's ability. The shaman could only work with patients who were cooperative and willing to participate in their recovery. As the shaman entered the altered state of consciousness aided by a steady, monotonous rhythm, the patient was able to gradually relax and participate fully in the moment. He moved from an awareness of pain, anxiety and fear to a sense of calm and optimism. This is the ideal mind/body state for healing.

Contemporary Use Of Music and Sound

There is an increasing use of music in medical facilities including intensive care units, pain management departments and dental offices. Memorial Sloan Kettering Cancer Center in New York, the University of Texas Health Science Center in San Antonio and Commonweal in Northern California are among the renown centers whose personnel agree that music decreases anxiety and manages pain making it easier for doctors to provide treatment and for medications to work.

Research of the effects of music on other disorders has been exciting. Recent studies show that listening to music can trigger memory and reality awareness in patients with dementia. It also has been found to help improve mobility of stroke patients. Music can also be used as a complement to allopathic medicine to bypass our psychic defenses. It can assist us in engaging emotionally and spiritually with our illness and recovery processes to assist healing.

According to the laws of physics, the universe is in a constant state of vibratory motion. Atoms, molecules and living organisms are vibrating structures. Plants, animals and humans are in a constant state of oscillation in rhythms of various beats and measures. Music and sound have vibratory effects on all cells and organs. They affect the brain and stimulate spiritual dimensions.

It has been discovered that most music is unconsciously written at the same pace and timing of the average heart rate. Some medical researchers have attributed, to this phenomenon, the fact that music can influence respiratory rate, blood pressure, stomach contractions and the level of stress hormones in the blood. Music is able to change a person's pulse, heart rate, rate of breathing and skin temperature in 45 to 50 seconds.

Damien's Story

Damien is a 47-year-old general contractor who owns a construction company that specializes in custom homes. He started in the trade at age 19 as a carpenter's helper in a company that built tract housing. He found that he enjoyed working with wood. He liked the smell of newly-milled boards and the feel of the wood after it had been planed and sanded. Because of his love for his job, he excelled in what he did. He worked with enthusiasm and was always willing to put in the long hours it took to get a project done. He quickly moved up the ranks to foreman and finally to project manager.

On a lunch break, one summer day, he and some fellow employees stopped at a convenience store to get drinks to have with their lunches. He was the first person through the check-out line and so, as he waited for his friends he glanced through the magazine rack. He noticed a magazine featuring custom homes.

As his flipped through it, he began to get excited. The excitement sparked a dream. Wouldn't it be pure joy to create such beautiful houses? Now, ten years after he had looked at that magazine, he was in his dream job.

He thoroughly enjoyed all aspects of running his own company and building the kinds of homes he loved. As his reputation spread, his business increased.

The enthusiasm of his potential customers made it difficult for him to turn people down. He had to hire more crews and work longer hours to manage all his projects. He was doing paper work late into the night.

He had less time to spend with his family. He always seemed to be eating on the run. He was no longer participating in the pick-up basketball games with his neighborhood buddies that he had always enjoyed. He had gained 20 pounds.

At his annual physical, his internist reported that in general he was in good health but his blood pressure was up and his cholesterol level was high. Damien was given a prescription for a cholesterol-lowering medication and a suggestion to lose some weight. At his follow-up appointment, two months later, his cholesterol level was down and so was his weight. But his blood pressure was still high. His doctor's admonishment was to find some time to relax; to have some fun.

When Damien got home, he told his wife about the results of his follow-up appointment. She mentioned that he seldom relaxed anymore. She reminded him of earlier days in their marriage. After dinner, he would put on some jazz, sit in a rocker on the porch and unwind from his workday. Damien was energized just thinking about it. He did just that, that very evening. He enjoyed it so much that he decided to make it part of his evening ritual.

At his next appointment with his doctor, his blood pressure was down. He has been able to consistently keep it in the normal range without medication.

The underlying principal of all modalities advocating sound activities to facilitate healing is that there is a tendency toward harmony by all entities in the universe. Sound and music tap into our mental and physical beings to adjust our inharmonious rhythms and return us to the state of synchronization with all of nature. When we are balanced and in harmony with the universe we are alert, serene and in the best of health.

The literature on balance reveals a number of studies on non-living things. If two metronomes are placed near each other in a room beating at different paces and rhythms they will moved toward a synchronization and eventually be keeping the same beat. The more powerful vibrations of one of the metronomes, when projected onto the second metronome, will cause the second metronome to begin to vibrate in resonance with the first. Pendulum clocks have the same response.

Physiological Effects of Sound and Music

Entrainment is the term used to describe bringing ourselves into harmony with the universe. Many healers - both Eastern and Western - believe that healing can be achieved by restoring the normal vibratory frequency of the diseased part of the body. Eastern medicine propones that illness is a manifestation of disharmony within the body. It is an imbalance in the cells in a specific organ such as the lungs or the heart. The vibrations formed by sound techniques are a means by which harmony could be realigned within the body on physiologic, as well as psychological levels.

There is a tendency by all entities in the universe toward harmony. We react in resonance with the vibrations and fluctuations in our surroundings. Our physiological functionings may be altered by the effect of sound waves whether that sound is produced by our own voices or by objects or instruments in our environment.

We, ourselves, are rhythm. The entire workings of our bodies require constant movement. Life requires that our hearts beat, our pulses throb and blood circulates freely. As we resonate on a cellular level we begin to heal physically, spiritually and emotionally. Because our bodies are a medley of sound, we can train ourselves to hear its messages. We can learn to listen for the sounds of disharmony within ourselves. This disharmony appears in the form of negative feelings and emotions. When we allow ourselves to be aware of our harmful emotions, we have the power to diffuse these feelings and transform our negative state into one that is calm, positive and conducive to healing.

Mitchell L. Gaynor, M.D., who uses sound along with allopathic medicine in his practice of oncology and integrative medicine, says, "I see the interplay and balance required to make music as a reflection of the harmonious interaction of the nervous, endocrine and immune systems in a healthy body." When a sense of peace and spiritual ease is achieved, the body is strengthened and is better able to handle the side effects of what-ever medical treatment it is undergoing and advance the process of both emotional and immunological healing.

Shifts In Awareness

Different sounds and tones can change a person's perspective and foster awareness of alternative solutions and greater possibilities. They can change the way a person reacts to particular circumstances. Slow, quiet, non - vocal rhythms reduce tension and stress. Faster varieties of sound and music heighten alertness and arousal.

A music genre called psycho-acoustic, used by some music thera-pists, is composed to alter brain-wave activity. The music is written so that pulses of sound that correspond with brain-wave frequencies are blended into a background of instrumental music, spoken words or sounds of na-ture. Creators of this type of music use sound pulses that are designed to coax the brain to lock on to a specific, calming brain-wave pattern. The frequency of the beats affects the level of consciousness.

Healing Techniques

Because there is a tendency for all things in the universe to move to-ward harmony, we react in resonance with the vibrations and fluctuations in our surroundings. Our physiological functionings have the possibilities of being altered by the impact of sound waves. These sound waves can be produced by objects or instruments in the environment. Equally effective are sounds made by our own voices chanting, singing or humming.

We receive healing benefits from sitting quietly and listening to rhythmic music and sounds. We also experience healing effects from participating in singing, chanting and playing a musical instrument.

• Listening To Sounds and Music

Find a time in your day or evening when you can have ten minutes of uninterrupted solitude. Choose a tape or compact disk of soft, gentle music that is soothing and relaxing. Select an instrumental piece without words. It could be something by a string quartet or a soft, rhythmic selection overlaid with the sounds of nature. Some people find bird sounds soothing; or the sound of ocean waves. Start the music playing at a volume that is loud enough to get your attention but not loud enough to be irritating. Sit in a favorite chair or recliner. You may prefer to lie on a bed or sofa supported by fluffy pillows. When you're comfortable, take three long, slender, therapeutic breaths. Breathe through your nose. With each exhalation, envision all stress and discomfort being carried out of your body. As you listen to the sound of the music, continue to breathe and rid yourself of all internal toxins.

Do this for ten minutes. Twenty minutes would have added therapeutic value and health benefits. You will emerge relaxed, alert and energized.

• Toning

Toning is an easy technique that takes just a few minutes a day and provides untold benefits. It is simply resonating one's own sound throughout one's body and soul. It releases tension and stimulates circulation and nerve energy. It can synchronize the brain waves to achieve profound states of relaxation.

To incorporate toning into your health regimen, sit quietly taking two or three deep, therapeutic breathes. Experience yourself beginning to let go of tension. On the next breath exhalation, emit a soft humming sound. Notice the emotional stress and physical pain leaving your body. For maximum health benefits do this for ten minutes a day. Alice Cash, Ph.D., of the University of Louisville Arts In Medicine program, incorporates drumming and sounds from other rhythmic instruments into toning. This has wondrous expressive and stress management effects.

• Making Music

Playing an instrument has profound effects on the body. It focuses and calms the mind. It decreases anxiety, loneliness and depression. All music is vibration. When you are holding and touching an instrument as you play, you get the vibratory benefits of resonance through both hearing the tones and by experiencing them through the sense of touch.

Even if you have never played an instrument, you can experience this phenomenon if you have access to a guitar. You can even try this in a music store using a guitar that's for sale. Sit comfortably in a chair. Hold the guitar in a playing position with the neck in your left hand. Don't touch the strings with that hand; just use it to lightly support the neck. With the body of the guitar resting lightly on your right knee, run your right hand gently over the strings in the area of the sound hole. As you repeat this movement, you will feel the vibrations stimulating your body at every point that it is making contact with the guitar. The sound waves will oscillate filling your entire being with extraordinary sensations.

By setting aside some time every day to synchronize your rhythms with the harmonies of the universe, you will stimulate your immune potential. You will meld with the cosmic healing powers and emerge physically and spiritually renewed.

Chapter 7

The Serenity of Movement

"On with the dance! Let joy be unconfin'd."

- - - Byron

The music begins. It crescendos. The group leader says, "Move to the music in any way you wish."

Participants begin tentatively taking small hesitant steps. Some of them haven't danced for a long time and are self-conscious about trying again. But they hear the music. It energizes their bodies. It reaches deep down to their souls. Their steps become larger and more rhythmic as their confidence increases with the swelling of the music. Patients in wheelchairs begin swaying their arms and nodding their heads in time to the music. Expressions are transformed into an other worldliness where leaping, bending and twirling is encouraged. Bodies are one with movement, with music, with space. Minds flow freely without thought ... with only experience.

This is an example of the increasing use of movement therapy in hospitals and rehabilitation centers in response to the research that movement is essential to good health and healing. The human body was created to move. It wasn't made to be stationary. The daily activities of our ancestors, as they foraged for food and ran from their predators, required their bodies to be fit and their muscles, flexible. Technological societies have reduced our need for the continual physical activity that used to be required for survival. It takes a lot less energy to walk through a supermarket, drive a car, put dirty clothes in a washer and wet clothes in a dryer. Since physical activity is no longer part of the daily routine for many of us, we often have to consciously contrive ways to maintain a well-functioning body.

If we maintain fitness we feel better, not only physically but mentally. We positively influence the quality and the length of our lives. Conversely, the lack of movement and exercise is associated with increased risk of disease and disabilities.

Movement directly influences and maintains our healing systems. Without movement we become sluggish, lethargic. Our bodies lose their capabilities to perform satisfactorily. Our internal organs are less effective.

Movement improves circulation and the efficiency of the heart's pumping capabilities. It maintains the elasticity of the arteries. Blood pressure is lowered. The cholesterol profile is improved. It facilitates digestion and weight loss. Movement tends the respiratory system. It increases the exchange of oxygen and carbon dioxide which helps the body eliminate metabolic wastes. It furthers elimination by promoting perspiration and movement of the intestines.

Diseases that come with aging are prevented and reduced in intensity. It delays arthritic symptoms. Bone density, necessary to prevent osteoporosis, is increased and maintained. It improves memory. It builds strength and increases flexibility. It boosts immunity to infection.

Movement and Chinese Medicine

In the self-sustaining activity of Taijiquan, movement keeps the Qi pulsating, full and strong. This strong-flowing Qi is essential to good health and proper body functioning. Qi is the Chinese word used to describe the vital life energy mentioned in every culture. "Good" Qi is available to our bodies in the air that we breathe and the food that we eat. "Bad" Qi is dispelled when we exhale. This bad Qi is then cleansed by the forces of the universe and continues on in the cosmic cycle of life.

Taijiquan is the movement activity that maintains the body's health and flexibility by keeping the Qi flowing through its meridians and collaterals. Smoothly flowing Qi helps the body to cleanse itself metabolically. It facilitates the efficient use of the food we eat to fuel our bodies. It balances the interconnections of our internal organs. It also helps to keep the mind calm and clear.

Taiji masters say that participating in movement exercises to keep the body healthy should be an enjoyable undertaking. Moving the body in a natural, uncontrived manner feels good. It gives us joy. Our energy is renewed. We relish the feelings produced by the effort and look forward to our next practice. Taijiquan is a system of movement that provides this type of pleasure.

Its benefits carry over into daily life. According to practitioners of traditional Chinese medicine, movement is essential for appropriate functioning of the body and is part of every regimen of health maintenance and healing.

Exercise and Western Medicine

Western physicians and medical scientists agree that a complete approach to fitness includes activities that improve endurance, strength and flexibility as well as body awareness. A weekly exercise program that includes twenty minutes of aerobic exercise four to five days and two sessions of weight training is often recommended by fitness experts.

However, for those of us who are less regimented, Andrew Weil, M.D., propones that walking is the ideal activity. According to Dr. Weil, walking requires the functional integration of sensory and motor experiences. It exercises our brains as well as our musculo-skeletal systems.

For example, the brain requires lots of information to maintain balance, to change positions and move over uneven surfaces. It needs information from the inner ear to keep oriented in three-dimensional space. Visual input and touch receptors are necessary to let us know what part of the body is in contact with the ground. In the brain, all of the information is processed by the cerebellum, which uses the input it receives to coordinate responses of muscles to the ever-changing requirements of movement and locomotion.

Both walking and Taijiquan require cross-patterning of the limbs. This generates electrical activity in the brain that has a harmonizing effect on the entire central nervous system. This special benefit is one that we do not always get from other kinds of exercise. When babies first learn to crawl, this movement of cross-patterning stimulates brain development. Some medical researchers have recommended crawling for adults as a way of speeding recovery from injuries.

Restful sleep is important for healing and recovery; exercise improves sleep. According to a Stanford University Medical School study conducted with older and middle-aged adults, the subjects reported sleeping better when they added regular movement to their routine. After sixteen weeks in a program of moderately intense exercise, they were able to fall asleep on the average of fifteen minutes earlier and sleep 45 minutes longer at night.

For optimum results, persistence is important. Most subjects didn't report improved sleep until after 16 weeks. The program entailed exercising four times a week. It included two sessions of organized aerobics with 30 minutes of endurance training, and two sessions in which the subjects were on their own, participating in 40 minutes of brisk walking or riding a stationary bike.

Regular moderate exercise also improves immunity. However, there is a converse side to the equation. Extremely intense bouts of exercise can depress the immune system and increase the risks of infection. Marathon runners' immunity is at its lowest just after a race. However, most of us get too little exercise rather than too much. Our risk of being sedentary far outweighs the risks of catching a cold because we exercise excessively.

Movement and Psychological Disorders and Stress

Our bodies are efficient machines that, when used the way they are meant to be used, appropriately perform all the functions needed to keep us well. Movement is essential to our bodies' ability to fulfill its purpose.

It not only facilitates physical well-being but affects mental health as well. Exercise releases chemicals in our bodies that reduce anxiety and depression. These chemicals are the body's natural opiates. Endorphins are stimulated to fight depression and improve frame of mind. Norepinephrine levels which are low in some depressed people, rise with exercise and help stabilize mood.

Not only does movement improve mood but it also increases the feelings of happiness, self-confidence and positive body image. It boosts optimism, reduces stress, increases energy and decreases fatigue. Exercise neutralizes tension and allows greater relaxation and sounder sleep.

Melissa's Story

Melissa is a third grade teacher in New York City. She lives in the Brooklyn borough of Park Slope. She gets up early every day, grabs a cup of coffee and a bagel and takes the train to her job in the city.

When she gets home in the late afternoon, she is tired from her day and the commute. However, her workday isn't over. She spends several hours each evening, correcting papers, reviewing her lesson plans, and preparing materials and teaching aids for the next day.

To revive and renew before her evening tasks, she changes into her running clothes as soon as she gets home, and jogs for about 45 minutes in Prospect Park down the street. She then takes a shower, eats a light supper and prepares for her next workday.

Melissa attributes her ability to stay energized throughout the evening and then fall quickly into a sound sleep, to her afternoon exercise break.

Movement Activities

Choose activities that you find enjoyable and during which you can achieve a focused, passive state of mind. It's essential, during your activity, not to debrief your workday or to mull over other concerns. Center your mind. Focus in the here and now. Allow yourself to notice the beauty around you. Take deep, healing breaths. If worries and concerns enter your mind, dismiss them telling yourself that you'll think about that later.

• Walking

Dr. Weil's recommendation for walking was discussed earlier in this chapter. The advantage of walking is that it can be done anywhere: on a country lane, along the beach, on a mountain trail, through residential neighborhoods, on the sidewalks of the city. It 's inexpensive. All you need are shoes with traction and clothes to accommodate the weather. In colder temperatures, dress in layers: a tee-shirt, a long sleeved outer shirt, a jacket. As you get into your walk and build up body heat, you can remove the layers of clothing to be more comfortable. A down vest is perfect for winter walks. It keeps the trunk of your body warm while leaving your arms free for easy movement.

If you haven't been participating in regular exercising in the past, begin slowly. Start with a five minute walk at a leisurely pace. As your stamina increases, build up to a 45 minute walk at a moderately brisk pace. Walking everyday is ideal for your physical and mental health.

If there are days when you can't walk as far as you'd like to because of other responsibilities or time constraints, do what you can without guilt. Just do something. A few minutes of walking is better than no walking at all. Take a quick walk around your yard or your apartment complex. Even this will improve your mood and energize your body.

• Dance

For many people, dance is the ultimate healing activity. It combines the healing powers of music, movement and meditation. It is easy to let the music surround you, embrace you and become the absolute focus of the moment. You find that you are leaving your day-to-day concerns behind to rise, sway and become one with air, space and time. You feel as if you're entering another dimension where you are no longer connected to materialism. You're not discouraged by physical limitations; you use whatever abilities you have to connect with the music, the movement and the universal forces.

Dancing for health and healing requires that you free your mind and your body to follow wherever the music leads you. There are no set patterns. The movement is choreographed by your soul. Your awareness soars to unimaginable heights. When you re-emerge, you feel lighter, more joyous and energized.

Jill Sonke Henderson, the dancer-in-residence at Shands Hospital at the University of Florida's Arts In Medicine program and the founder and director of the Dance For Life Program at the University of Florida, recommends the following steps to begin to use dance for the maintenance of health and healing.

- Find someplace to dance, an area where you have enough space to move around and be free.
- Select music that you love and to which you like to move.
- Warm up by stretching for a few minutes.
- Connect with the energy in your body.
- Allow your body to move spontaneously. Follow the movement.
- Follow the rhythm of the music.
- Start to dance with explorations in pure music.
- Allow the divine dancer to move within you.

Dance can lead to a higher meditative state. In that state you will begin to visualize your body and spirit becoming one with the forces of the universe. You will experience yourself falling deeply into the center of a spiral of glorious movement and sound. You will feel yourself receiving the energy of the earth. As you release yourself to the powers of dance your body will be free; your spirits will soar.

• Taijiquan

"No pain, no gain" is the mantra of many exercise buffs. They push themselves and force their bodies beyond limitations to gain that extra mile. By contrast, beneficial movement can be enjoyable, spontaneous and uplifting. It can transfer what we learn to optimum body movement in daily life. Taijiquan is a Chinese exercise/movement system that does this. It increases strength of not only muscles but of bones and the internal organs: the heart, lungs and kidneys. In fact, health problems are often the result of more muscle strength than the lack of it. Excessive concentrations of muscle strength constrict organs, blood vessels and the muscles themselves. They impede and decrease the ability of the blood to provide nutrients and oxygen to the extremities of the body and cause irregularity in the removal of waste. Muscle constrictions disrupt the natural flow of Qi. This disruption impedes good health.

Taijiquan improves flexibility which lets us move through the full range of movement allowed by the physical structure of our bodies. Physical capability is often diminished by injury, misuse or lack of use of our bodies. It is often possible to regain full functioning through the gentle movements of this system.

There is also an increase in the body's coordination, reflexive actions and balance. We learn to use our mind to direct the body parts in moving efficiently and harmoniously. We react to situations appropriately without conscious thought. Proper body reactions result from the repetitive practice of similar coordinated movements. Taijiquan provides this practice.

Because this system has specific patterns of movements, it isn't possible to provide information in this section that would allow you to become a proficient practitioner of Taijiquan. You would need to find an accomplished Taiji master to teach you the exercises and take you through the combinations. Video tapes are also available. However, some principles of the movements will get you started on informal practice.

Start by centering; by standing quietly with bowed head. Remove all thought except body awareness. Take three, deep, healing breaths. Begin moving slowly. Throughout the entire practice, movement is slow and fluid. Taijiquan combinations are generally those of animals; their stances, bends, squats, turns and forward and backward motions. See yourself as an animal that you like. Imitate its movements in slow motion. Favorite Chinese animals are the crane, the tiger and the monkey.

Taijiquan also has a system of martial arts. Some of the martial arts movements have been incorporated into the practice for health and healing. These movements generally consist of attack and avoid techniques. Think of attacking with pushing and punching. Avoid by movements that will ward off or elude blows. When using these combinations in your practice, alternate attacking movements and avoidance movements. Remember to move in slow motion.

•Movement In Daily Life

We all use movement everyday. However, we can increase our opportunities to participate in this beneficial activity by making some simple choices. Instead of driving your car, walk or bike to work. If you must drive, park as far away as reasonably possible and give yourself the pleasure of a short walk to your destination. Climb stairs. Pull weeds. Cut grass with a push mower. Use a full range of motion while doing house cleaning or other chores. Breathe deeply. Think wonderful thoughts. Bend, twist, turn. Stretch your arms up to the sky. Experience the pure joy of moving through life.

Chapter 8

The Serenity of Art

"Art is not an end in itself, but a means of addressing (our) humanity."
- - - *Moussorgsky*

Jeanne paused and looked up as her therapist entered the room. She smiled as she went back to molding the damp clay with the tips of her fingers. Her face was calm; almost beatic. Her body was relaxed and supple. She was impelled by an inner sense of serenity. This was a big change from her presentation of four weeks prior when her mother first took her to The Healing Center where art was used both for therapy and for healing.

At that time, Jeanne had just learned that she had leukemia. Her 14-year-old mind swirled with confusion, anger and despair. Her feeling tone was one of fear and tension. Her mother had majored in art in college and had taken a beginning art therapy class as an elective. In her own devastation at the news of her daughter's illness, she reached out to the only area she knew well. Maybe art would retard the process of her daughter's illness and even assist in cure.

Participating in art involves the mind, the emotions and many parts of the body. A total melding of these entities with a focus on the art activity, returns the body to equilibrium; to the place of balance that is the optimum condition for the maintenance of good health and healing.

When we create, places deep in our souls are stimulated. We can go from hostility and loneliness to extraordinary inspiration and awareness. This change in attitude affects our quality of life and stimulates the physical resources that could lengthen life and help us heal. Our spirit is awakened. Our bodies, minds and souls are strengthened. Natural healing ability intensifies. Life energy surges.

Our outlook on life becomes more positive. We are freer, more open to greater possibilities. The act of creating peels off and sluffs away layers of negative emotions: depression, anxiety, pessimism, hostility, anger. We are left with the freedom to experience and express joy. We release what Dr. Michael Samuels and Mary Lane, RN, call the inner healer.

In their work with art and healing, they found that creativity and healing come from the same source -- the soul. Their research shows that a person making art and a person healing have the same physiology, the same brain wave patterns and the same states of consciousness.

Art can also help a patient manage pain. A person who is ill can reduce his pain by participating in a creative act. He can decrease the intensity of his symptoms. This reduction of symptoms is then carried over into the rest of the patient's day. He feels less pain and discomfort. Depression and anxiety lift. Mental and physical energy is restored and enthusiasm heightens.

In this chapter, the making and viewing of art is discussed, not as it pertains to art therapy but as it is used in healing. Art therapists generally use art for interpretation, personality growth and insight. When it is used for healing, it reaches the deep recesses of the body and soul to summon the body's healing powers.

Ben's Story

Ben was at an all-time high. Life was great. He was a twenty-eight year old man enjoying every minute of his life. He was in a job that he liked, working for the city as a fireman. After ten years of pursuing his education and work goals, his professional life was just where he wanted it to be. His personal life was also going well. He had recently reconnected with his high school sweetheart and they planned to be married.

Now Ben was writhing in pain. Pain killers didn't help much. They relieved the agony but he was never free from the sensitivity and discomfort of the burns that covered two-thirds of his body.

There had been a fire in a five story building downtown, and his unit had responded. He and his team had gone in and were fighting the blaze on the second floor when the direction of the fire shifted and came back at him in full force. He was instantly engulfed in flames.

He woke up in the hospital's burn unit with a doctor and several nurses hovering over him. The pain was excruciating. During the next few weeks, Ben was seldom left alone. A member of his medical team was always with him monitoring his vital signs, administering medications and trying to ease his discomfort. They were pleased with the progress of his healing. Yet, his constant pain zapped his physical and mental energy. Depression set in.

One morning, after the bustle of breakfast, a bed bath and the freshening of his linens and his room, he was visited by the staff social worker. She sat in a chair next to his bed and asked him how he was doing. He found her easy to talk to and told her about his pain and his feelings of hopelessness. He told her how confining he found the hospital room. Even though he was injured and realized that he needed to be there to receive appropriate care, he had always been a person who loved being outdoors. He missed the feeling of the breeze blowing, the sounds of rustling trees and the sunshine warming his body. As she listened, the social worker sketched on a pad using pencils and crayons. At the end of the visit, she handed the drawing to him.

It was an outdoor scene with a clear sky, trees and a lake. Vibrant colors of blue, yellow and pink swirled in the heavens. In the midst of the color was the face of a man that looked very much like Ben. The expression on his face was one of serenity.

When Ben looked at the picture, he smiled. Somehow, he felt uplifted. The drawing wasn't professionally done, in fact it was quite primitive. Yet, it warmed a place deep down in his soul. He asked to have it placed on the wall next to his bed. Whenever he looked at it, he felt a sense of peace. It was similar to the feeling of caring that he got when his mother or his fiancee were in the room. It provided a moment of freedom from pain.

Simply looking at art in various forms can be therapeutic. If viewing is done in a relaxed, leisurely way and the observer is open to emotional awareness, the curative properties within her can be stimulated. As she concentrates on the beauty of the painting or object, on its color and its flow of movement, as she becomes in tune with the artist's statement, she is transformed elsewhere. A favorable environment for healing emerges and her body responds with renewed vigor.

In Ben's story, he was involved in what is known in the art healing community as transpersonal art. It is art of communication, of connectedness. The art healer creates something specifically for one person or a group of people. The artist who develops his piece with caring and compassion for the recipient infuses the object with a force so powerful that it can activate healing energies. The person receiving the gift connects with the empathy of the artist and is comforted and energized.

• Art Activities

Being creative is as simple as seeing the beauty, mystery and artistic qualities of life through your own eyes. As you participate in an art activity, whether as an artist or as a viewer, remember to breathe therapeutically. Take three slow, deep breaths, inhaling fully before you begin. This helps you to center, to focus within yourself and prepare mentally and physically; to be completely in the moment of the activity.

• Drawing

With sketchbook and colored pencils in hand, sit in a place that is peaceful for you. It can be in a lovely room, in the garden or on a lake. Sit quietly. Take long, slow breaths and just survey the scene. Notice the colors and the shapes. Be aware of your feelings that are evoked by your surroundings. When you're ready, begin. Capture the things you notice: the colors, the forms, the movement.

What you draw doesn't have to be exact representations. In fact, renown artists who have spoken to our souls have worked in non-representational styles. Monet worked in Impressionism with a blurred, misty quality. Picasso's drawings incorporated figments of his mind. Georgia O'Keefe painted flowers and plants that were larger than life and in colors that were more vivid than reality.

You'll soon find yourself swept away by the flow of your participation. You will be so absorbed and entranced by your surroundings and your creativity, that time will pass without notice. You will emerge invigorated. Your heart will sing.

•Therapeutic Painting

A particularly healing way of using paint is simply splashing color on a canvas. Be sure to use a large ground cloth so you don't have to worry about getting paint on the floor or ground. You can use a canvas on an easel or laying flat on the floor a la Jackson Pollack. He often used large canvasses, cans of house paint and sticks as his tools. He would dip his sticks into the paint cans and dribble the paint over his canvas. He dribbled, splashed and swirled to his heart's content until his painting felt "finished." After a painting he emerged satisfied and energized.

If you would prefer to work with brushes, you can evoke the same healing properties by sitting or standing in front of an easel. Using acrylic paints allows you to thin the paint with water to get a consistency you like. Stand in front of your canvas. Close your eyes and take three therapeutic breaths. Then open your eyes and choose a favorite color. Use your brush any way you like. Swirl the paint over the canvas. Paint in squiggles, in straight lines. Use sponges to dab on paint for a different texture. Change colors, mix tones. Release the child within you to do whatever you want. Find that place deep inside of your heart where no one is judging you, where there is no criticism. Joyously use the paint to arouse your healing spirit.

•Crafts

Doing crafts can summon the same feelings of joy, serenity and well-being. Choose materials you love and that bring you a sense of wonder. You could make necklaces and bracelets using sparkling glass beads that shimmer in the sunlight. If you like to fill your house with things that evoke feelings of warmth and comfort, make wreaths of seeds, pods and dried flowers. Consider looking for interesting pieces of wood and revealing its beauty by shaping, sanding and oiling.

These activities are healing and therapeutic. You need only to stay in the moment. Emerge with the immediate joy of creating. Suspend your worries and concerns. Experience, just for now, the wonder of forming something lovely; a healing amulet. Keep it for your own healing or share it with someone else. You will both benefit from its healing force.

Chapter 9

The Serenity of Writing

"You must write for yourself, above all."
        - - - *Gustave Flaubert, 1858.*

Do you wonder why you might write? You may discover a hidden talent and become a novelist or poet. You may even develop a large readership, sell a lot of books and become rich and famous. However, in reality, it's unlikely that you will use the information in this chapter to become a professional writer. What you will do is peel off the layers of disturbing, subconscious experiences, thoughts and feelings that are hindering your ability to find peace. You will heal your mind and soothe your soul.

Writing is self-therapy. Psychotherapists agree that writing on a regular basis is stress-reducing and healing. Mini-traumas from the past require psychic energy. We use this energy to avoid thinking about past hurts and disappointments and to mask the feelings that are evoked when we do think about them. We struggle to fight them off and keep them buried. We can even relegate them to our subconscious and assume that we have resolved them and they are no longer part of our existence. But they haven't disappeared. We're just doing a good job of not letting them surface.

Jared's Story

Jared is a 32-year old insurance salesman who works for a national company. He is ethical, hard-working and well-respected. He has a wife and a new baby. They have a tight circle of good friends with whom they socialize two or three times a month. Jared's wife reports that he is generally mild mannered and supportive. He is never critical. He asks nothing of her and never makes unreasonable requests. However, whenever something unexpected occurs for him, whether it's not being able to immediately find his keys in his pocket or being unable to fit his car into a parking spot, he goes into an uncontrollable rage. These rages never last more than one or two minutes. While they're occurring, he is never violent or abusive to anyone. However, the outbursts are inappropriate; there is too much anger and passion expended over relatively small incidents.

The impetus behind the rage episode is not really the incident of the moment. It is all similar frustrations of the past that were not dealt with and were stored in his psyche, unresolved, waiting to be released. Jared had so much unresolved emotionality that it was eventually difficult for him to continue to hold his anger in check. When an unexpected incident would occur, no matter how small, he would have to deal with the matter by tapping into some of the psychic energy that he was using to hold all unresolved emotions in check. This would allow some of the feelings behind past hurts and frustrations to escape and burst forth in uncontrollable rage. Observers assumed that he was angry at the immediate problem when in actuality he was discharging pent-up emotionality from the past.

Jared played racquetball with his friend Brian, every Saturday morning. They would have breakfast in the club's coffee shop after the game. During a match, it wasn't unusual that Jared's anger and frustration would escalate every time he missed a shot or lost a point. On this particular morning, Jared's emotional intensity was particularly high and his outbursts, more frequent than usual.

At breakfast, Brian, who worked in the field of vocational rehabilitation, asked, "What's going on?"

Jared responded, "I just get so mad when I miss a shot."

As they talked more about Jared's past week, he realized that he seemed to be more frustrated than usual. He was very quick to lose his temper and take his irritation out on others. His wife had even mentioned it .

Brian responded, "Sounds like you're letting things build up. They're getting to you." He went on to explain a technique that he suggested to his clients when they were especially anxious or short-tempered. He recommended that they spend some time, everyday, writing down their thoughts, worries and frustrations.

Jared decided to give it a try. He had always considered himself calm and mild-mannered and was beginning to be embarrassed by his outbursts. He began keeping a journal and making notes in it everyday. He journaled for the first 15 minutes of his workday while he had a cup of coffee. He felt better after the first morning of writing and noticed his internal pressures decreasing as he continued this activity.

Jared still journals. His stress level is lower and his outbursts are almost nonexistent. He noticed that if he goes two or three days without journaling, his tension begins to mount. When that happens, he remembers that he should get back to his writing.

Both the small and the larger traumas that affect our psyches, provide negative feelings that accumulate. Our bodies become tense with the need to keep everything under control and present to others in ways that we view as acceptable. These incidences can be catastrophic such as the death of a parent. They can be milder in intensity as being teased when we were children for wearing glasses. As more and more of these occurrences happen without resolution, an increasing amount of energy must be expended to keep them under wraps. This causes emotional and physical tension which can lead to physical problems.

Medical scientists have been looking for ways to reduce symptoms and cure diseases that are known to be exacerbated by chronic stress and tension. One particular study examined whether or not writing had an effect on the intensity of physical problems associated with asthma. The study required asthma patients to write for twenty minutes a day for three days. They were to write about a traumatic or intense life event. Researchers found that writing provided relief from internal stress. There was also an improvement in lung functioning. The patients who used writing as part of their treatment process, reported fewer symptoms, fewer doctor visits, improved mood and a more positive outlook on life.

The Power of Writing to Heal

Writing can be used to release debilitating emotional material and to begin to free up psychic energy for more productive uses. It can release our healing energy, referred to as Qi in traditional Chinese medicine, and allow it to resonate in our bodies, minds and spirits. Writing can unclog the flow of Qi so that it pulsates strong and unhampered through our internal systems. It also unshackles the full range of human emotions - hurt, resentment, fear, despair, sadness, anger, obsession - that often clog up our psyche and prevent us from finding peace of mind.

Writing when we are experiencing difficulties is cathartic and healing. It compels us to confront the negative emotions that are sapping our energies. We begin to find it less necessary to suppress our emotional fears; we are encouraged to face our pain. Writing opens the doorway to the spirit of infinite possibilities. We develop awareness and insight. We're able to identify appropriate solutions to our physical and emotional concerns. Writing is the vehicle for revealing and exposing whatever is in our hearts.

When you write to heal, use your own words to address your truth, deepen your self-understanding and expand your creative imagination. The traditional model for healing through writing is one in which your inner process is revealed and becomes accessible to you and to your therapist. It is free association in written form. It may help you deal more easily, with grief, anger, sadness or emotional pain then would traditional psychotherapy because it is sometimes easier to put thoughts, feelings and beliefs on paper than to verbalize them directly to another person.

Current use of writing in healing runs the gamut of the traditional written free association to writing with more structure. Each method has its own power. Explore the different forms to see what works best for you.

The process of free writing, writing whatever comes into your aware-ness, is healing in itself. Confess what you are trying to keep inside. Inhibi-tion takes mental and physical energy and weakens the cardiovascular and immune systems. Recognize and admit your true feelings and reflective thoughts. Share them, admit them, reflect on them and accept them. Ac-knowledge your fears, faults and failures and take responsibility for hurt-ing another soul. Write about negative thoughts along with positive ones. This is not to be viewed as a self-affirmation. This is a confession of the truth. Addressing negative feelings in writing strengthens emotional and physical health. After your "confession" you will be more relaxed and bal-anced. Qi will surge with healing force and without obstruction.

"Writing To Heal" Techniques

Along with free writing, there are other methods that you can use. You may enjoy journaling, or writing poetry and short stories. Before at-tempting any of these activities, make sure that you have a comfortable, pleasant place to write. Also important is a block of time during which you will be able to be alone without interruption. Allow at least fifteen minutes for your "writing-to-heal" session. Set up a specific writing schedule. A colleague of mine gets up an hour earlier than the rest of the family to have some time for herself. She implements her writing plan during this early morning hour three days a week - Monday, Wednesday and Friday for fif-teen minutes a session. To be truly therapeutic, writing periods need to be regular and consistent. Writing occasionally when you feel the need, is less healing in the long run.

Writing makes it possible to express your full range of feelings, doubts and insights. Explore your deepest thoughts and acknowledge the feelings behind them. Write about those feelings. Address and release all your feelings of sadness, hurt, anger, guilt, fear and resentment.

Don't inhibit your writing by planning to share it with anyone. Your "healing writing" is for your eyes only. Write continuously. Don't edit your writing. Don't worry about spelling or grammar. Don't cross out or erase. If you run out of thoughts, write about running out of thoughts and not having anymore to say but continue writing for at least fifteen minutes. Apply these rules to everything you write for healing.

If you are coping with a current trauma, don't expect to feel good immediately. The feelings of sadness and depression will decrease slowly over time. Writing will hasten healing.

•Journalizing

Journalizing is similar to the ferreting about in both the past and the present that occurs when we journal. However, the concentration in journalizing is on the day's events. Therefore, it is best done in the late afternoon or evening. Date your entry. Recount the day's events that had an impact on you. Write about things that made you happy and brought you joy. Note what evoked anger, anxiety or sadness. Record perceptions, feelings. If an event of today triggers an association to the past, write about that past event but don't ruminate about the connection. Just write the thoughts and feelings that come to mind.

Ask yourself a question, make a statement or recount a plan you have for your life that you are having difficulty implementing. Reread your journal entries regularly, every two weeks as an example, or monthly. This gives you the opportunity to notice continual concerns and recurring themes. After several journalizings of a recurring hurt or concern, the intensity of feelings will decrease and you will be able to emotionally let it go or take action to change the situation.

• Poetry

More than any other kinds of writings, poetry reaches the depths of our inner souls. It stimulates our sensitivity, growth and transformation. The sounds and rhythms of poetry can penetrate a psychic level that cognitive thinking cannot. It heals. It expands the possibilities for growth and change. It awakens a new appreciation for life.

Laurie's Story

Laurie was in agony. What should have been a routine angiogram, became an excruciatingly painful experience when her aorta was abraded during the procedure. She was kept comfortable for two days with morphine but was sent home from the hospital with ongoing pain. This pain lasted for three weeks before it began to subside as the abrasion started to heal. Her husband was frustrated in his inability to do anything to provide relief and finally said, "How can I help you?"

As the pain began to lift, allowing Laurie to be more coherent and less focused on the agony, she wrote the following poem.

How can you help me?
Touch my hand
Look at me with joy
Smile.
Tell me a funny story
Caress my cheek
Squeeze my shoulder.
Pick a flower for my table.
Sit with me in silence
Support me in my pain.

Poetry can be created any way you want. It can rhyme or be written in free verse. Traditional poetry appreciation classes discuss meter and iambic pentameter. However, the inspiring poet or one who writes for healing can ignore all guidelines. The only criteria is writing from the heart.

Poetry to heal is easy to do. Write about whatever comes to mind. You could write about a time, a place, a person. Add some descriptive words. Reflect on your feelings. And there, you have it. Here is an example if you are still hesitant to get started.

What does autumn bring?
Crisp air - muted days
of burnt orange - yellow.
Why this sadness?
A loss ... of what?

Writing Haiku, a Japanese form of poetry, is a good way to get started if you need more structure to get you going. Each poem is just three lines. The structure is provided by the exact number of syllables in each line. Line one and three have five syllables. Line two has seven. All you have to remember is 5 - 7 - 5.

Stand in the garden
Feel the sun's gentle caress
Tension melts away.

＊ ＊ ＊

Frustrating workday
I am anxious to go home
Who blocked my car in?

＊ ＊ ＊

I think about us
Will we have another day?
Or will God call me?

•Short Stories

Take a few minutes to do the following exercise. Imagine an animal. Describe it in two or three sentences. What is it about to do? How do you feel about that?

Stories come from our reality, our memory and our subconscious. Whatever enters our conscious mind needs to be dealt with, ruminated over and resolved. Creating stories is a safe non-threatening way to do this. It allows us to remain distanced if our fictional Sally gets dumped by the man she had been dating for two years and who had often hinted at marriage. Writing about Sally's experiences and feelings helps us tap into our own fears. It allows us to face our feelings, doubts and inclinations in a safe way. It then encourages us to resolve them and learn from those experiences.

Writing activities, if practiced daily or at least four to five times a week, will provide you with an on-going sense of well being. You will be recharged with energy and enthusiasm for the opportunities and challenges of life. You will improve your physical and mental health.

Chapter 10

The Serenity of Nature

"Nature never did betray the heart that loved her."
- - - Wordsworth

On a chilly Sunday morning, just as dawn begins to break, David starts up the trail. There is only enough light to reveal shadows along the path but he walks with confidence because he knows the mountain well. As a child, he lived in a house 100 yards from the trailhead and used Mt. Rubidoux as his playground. It was also a place where he could be alone when he wanted to, where he could find silence and solitude, where the only distractions were the twittering of birds, the gentle caress of a cool breeze and the swiftness of insects scurrying across the path.

David is a cardiologist with a 50-hour a week workload. He is unwavering in his choice to reserve Sunday mornings for his trek up the mountain. "It's where I find peace ... where I recuperate from a stressful week. There, I am renewed and can then prepare to meet the next week's challenges."

Why do we, along with David, find peace of mind when we are outdoors in a natural setting? Why do we feel invigorated and free from stress? Scientists tell us that we're only one part of a larger whole that includes everything in the universe. We are interconnected to the earth, animals, water, sun, moon, wind, air, stars and planets. Not only are we connected but we're dependent on each other for existence.

The movements of the universe affect each entity within it. When the sky darkens and rainclouds form, eventually releasing their contents, the rain permeates the soil, nurturing the plants. The richer the soil from a good supply of water, minerals and fertilizing excrement from animals and insects, the more nutritious the plants that we eat to keep ourselves alive and healthy.

Soil supports life. The health of the land is directly connected with the health of all creatures. The deeper, darker, more fertile the soil, the healthier and stronger the growth of living things. None of the entities can live well without the others. Neither can any survive if they don't interact reciprocally, using whatever each needs but also replenishing and protecting the unused portions.

All of the elements of the universe work together to sustain one another. Through this collaboration we are provided with air, plants and water - our life's sustenance. We are all interconnected. When we look at a single cell of a human body we see the influence of the universe. The sun, moon, stars and earth each have a part in maintaining the cell's ceaseless rhythm. When we explore the mind we find all the archaic urges of both human and animal primitive life. It is obvious that the human entity is the meeting place for the melding of all universal forces.

Ancient people were aware of this link. They recognized that everything they did, every act they performed, was as much a part of the whole universal milieu as were the movements of the sun, the wind and the ocean. So when they trod across the land, took water from the streams or removed branches from trees, they did it in a manner that did not disturb the natural life progression of earth's bounty.

When they gathered plants for food or medicine, they picked the leaves and stems and left the roots to continue to grow. If they wanted the roots, they didn't harvest the younger plants. They left them to propagate so there would be continual availability. They gathered seeds to use to replenish the crop.

The breakdown of our connection to the other entities in nature began with the civilization of man. We learned that we could make ourselves more comfortable by building structures that would protect us from the other elements. We built dams and aqueducts so we could take water from its natural settings and divert it to deserts, changing the properties of arid land and making it more serviceable for our own use.

However, the more we separated ourselves from the cold, the rain and the wind, the more we began to view those elements as inconvenient and even detrimental to the comforts we were beginning to enjoy. Thus began the plan to conquer and control the natural forces.

Unfortunately, success has had its price. Houses that have been built in dry riverbeds have been swept away when the riverflow was restored by the balance of nature. Buildings constructed in niches cut into seaside cliffs have tumbled into the ocean during a season of heavy rains. People who were working in buildings with windows sealed to make more efficient use of artificial heat and cooling began developing physical problems and illnesses. Attempts to separate ourselves from nature have resulted in increasingly adverse consequences.

The more we isolate ourselves from the other entities in our universe, the less we benefit from connectedness and reciprocity. Isolation not only deprives us of benefits but creates physical and emotional problems. Many people in society are finding that they're not as content in life as they would like to be. They often experience tension, sadness or dissatisfaction at levels that interfere with their enjoyment of the moment. They can't concentrate. They don't perform optimally on tasks or projects.

Re-establishing our connection to the other entities of nature would be a start in the healing of our bodies and our souls. It would decrease our stress and improve concentration. Blending the natural synchronization of our rhythms with those of the other elements in our surroundings fosters harmony and tranquillity. When we understand the ebb and flow of the changing seasons, our awareness of our own seasonal cycles will increase. We will then be able to drift comfortably according to our natural cadence. We will be in balance with the universe and with ourselves.

The Seasonal Cycle of Life

Our rhythms are homologous to the seasons of nature. Spring is associated with renewal, fertility and reawakening. Mother Nature warms the earth to signal the beginning of the season. Snow melts; frost is no longer a concern. Seeds germinate pushing tender plants from the undersoil to pop out into the sunlight. Bulbs burst through the ground. Hibernating animals awaken, flexing their muscles and begin the season's search for food and mating partners. All the elements of nature, including humankind, are renewed. There is a revitalization of our bodies and our souls.

In ancient times, Spring was a period to celebrate the rebirth of the soil and the plants. In old England, people would glorify the season by gathering together to share food, see each other again after a long winter of keeping close to their own homes, dance around the maypole and tingle with the excitement of sexual awakening. There was a regeneration of enthusiasm and energy.

Summer provides extra light to work and frolic. Europeans of long ago had celebrations with revelry, games and merriment to mark the summer solstice, the year's longest day of sunshine. There is evidence everywhere of vigorous growth and expansion. The land is vibrant with exuberant color. Our energy converges with the energies of everything around us and we are renewed. Vitality increases as the sunlight permeates our entire beings. Integrated with nature, our bodies are strengthened; our hearts are full of joy.

Autumn is a rich, full season. The plants ripen and reach maturity. Throughout the ages, agriculture communities participated in the harvest and were thankful when the fruits of their labor resulted in abundance. The people celebrated with feasting, drinking and giving thanks.

Autumn was also a season of reflection. The villagers knew by experience that they were about to enter a period of dormancy. The coming season would force them to slow down and let their bodies recuperate from the continual activity in which they engaged during the other three periods of the year. This break would allow them to recharge and emerge again, invigorated with energy and motivation. They knew that the soil would also be at rest and would not be providing them with unending sustenance. If they were to survive through those dormant months, they had to preserve some of the offerings of the harvest to help themselves exist through the season.

Autumn was a time to plan and prepare. People knew that with appropriate preparation, they would be able to gather and preserve sufficient food and fuel to sustain themselves through this harshest time of the year. They knew the coming period would be cold and dark. Yet, it was part of the natural cycle of existence and the following season would again bring renewal of the land.

To indigenous people, Winter was a time to stay closer to home. Families gathered together for warmth and companionship. There was more time to interact, to get to know each other better. There were more opportunities to be in tune with the thoughts, feelings and needs of each person in the household. Family members had time to provide one another with comfort and nurturance.

Winter also gave each person time to center; to look within himself and become aware of his own needs and desires. He could reflect on his strengths, his abilities. He could ponder his place in life, dreaming of his own re-emergence which would occur with the reawakening of the land. He was able to participate in activities of art and music that would render happiness and serenity. His body would use this resting period to start its renewal. His soul would begin to sing at the approach of Spring and he would be eager to burst forth with new resolve.

Nature's Healing Power

Irma had recently had a mastectomy. Her oncologist reported that the operation was successful. He was able to remove all the cancer. She was allowed to go home after a three-day stay in the hospital and given prescriptions to guard against infections. She was also given some pain medication to use as needed. She had instructions for bathing the area and a schedule of follow-up appointments. Her responses to the doctor sounded positive and optimistic. Her husband listened intently and was eager to help.

At her first follow-up appointment, one week after surgery, progress was appropriate. The wound was clean and uninfected. Her husband had been ministering to her and helping her keep the area clean because raising her arm was difficult and painful. At two weeks post-surgery, the wound was still clean but did not show the normal signs of healing that would be expected at this stage. After three weeks, evidences of infection began to emerge. She was put on an aggressive antibiotic regimen and appointments were scheduled closer together. The nurse mentioned to the cardiologist that Irma seemed depressed. The doctor referred her to my office to determine whether or not there was an emotional component that interfered with the curing process.

At the first session, Irma burst into tears. She said that six days after she was released from the hospital, she discovered that her husband had been having an affair. Although he assured her that it was over, she couldn't stop thinking about it. My concern was that the worries and stress created by the situation could be retarding cure. The treatment plan we created together included some individual sessions and then a combination of weekly individual sessions and conjoint sessions with her husband. After three weeks, she reported feeling better during the sessions and for one or two days following the appointment. However, between visits, the sadness and despair returned. She wanted to increase the frequency of her appointments but her insurance carrier would not pay for more than one session per week.

During one of her appointments, Irma was taught a simple technique to reduce her anxiety and to elevate her mood. She would allow for two 15-minute periods a day to simply sit and commune with nature. One session would take place right after breakfast and the other would be in the late afternoon. Her only requirement was to sit in a comfortable chair outdoors or, in inclement weather, next to a window overlooking her garden. She was to take three deep, calming breaths and then just be. She was to let her mind drift among the entities of nature: the sounds of the birds, the pungent odor of the eucalyptus trees, the curative heat of the sun. She was to do this everyday that she did not attend a psychotherapeutic session.

She faithfully followed this regimen and was eventually able to help free herself from the depression and anxiety that she was experiencing between sessions. Her wound also began to mend.

Irma attributes her recovery to the treatment of her internist and oncologist, her individual and conjoint psychotherapy sessions and her own participation that assisted in the strengthening of her immune potential through daily connectedness with nature.

When we're in an outdoors setting we're in our natural place. We're among the entities that are supportive of us, that sustain us and give us life. However, like a youth in her early teens who rebels against the dictates of her family, we often resist nature with angry frustration. We view a heavy rain or swirling dust as a dire inconvenience that may prevent us from an outdoor activity in "ideal weather."

Yet, whatever our attitude, nature goes on to strengthen its properties that are essential to us. Plants use the richness of the soil and the power of the sun to become nutritious food for our use. Water allows us to cleanse our outer and inner selves helping to purify, nurture and revive us. If we embrace nature instead of defying it, it soothes our bodies and heals our souls.

The simple act of breathing is life-sustaining. When we breathe deeply while outdoors, we connect with the air, the skies and the heavens. If we are in an area with trees, the air is fresher still. The surrounding plants continually fulfill one of its purposes, that of cleansing the atmosphere.

Being in remote, natural settings also provides us with time-out from life's stressors. We momentarily separate from our worries and responsibilities. If we continue to breathe deeply and center, using all our senses to fully experience our surroundings, we transcend to a higher level of awareness. At this level, our psyches blend with the spiritual energy of all that surrounds us - of the animals, the plants, the air, the rocks. We feel stress draining from our bodies. The tension is replaced with peace and tranquillity. We are inspired and invigorated. We're on a level of consciousness that encourages the curing of our bodies and the awakening of our souls.

Ways To Connect With Nature

Nature is all around us and ways to connect with it are unending. I'll discuss three of them that are easy to implement: walking, gardening and tending indoor plants. As you read about each activity, you will undoubtedly think of others that would be appealing to you.

• Walking

Dr. Pamela Peeke, assistant professor of medicine at the University of Maryland in Baltimore, suggests spending some time, everyday, walking among trees or beside water. "People who do so are content. Nature is the best natural anti-depressant." Walking in nature is calming. As you walk, experience the moment. The more connected we are with nature, the more connected we are with ourselves. The Chinese call walking along paths and experiencing with all our senses "walking meditation."

We receive a special benefit when walking in sacred places. These places have become sacred because, over the years, they became invested with great spirit. These are places where people and their descendants lived for centuries, caring for, respecting and loving the land. Here we experience a feeling of well being, comfort and peace. We are nurtured by the loving spirits of all who were there before. Our souls are enriched. Love and goodwill fill our minds and bodies.

Walking near the ocean is particularly beneficial. All life emerged from the sea and when walking along the shore, we feel a connection that is overwhelming in the comfort it provides. As the tides and the winds move in from the ocean, the rhythm of the surf beating against the shore invigorates us. A potent rush of vitality surges through our bodies. We are home, nurtured and energized.

There are places where spiritual presence is so dynamic that we are affected by its powers just by being there; places such as the forests and remote beaches of Hawaii, the deserts around Sante Fe and the rises of Stonehenge. When you are in these sacred places you find yourself standing silently, breathing deeply and becoming one with the entities that surround you. The spirits in nature are inviting you to pause for a moment, connect with them, be nurtured and revitalized. When you heed their call, you leave with a renewed sense of calm, serenity and inspiration.

• Gardening

Since ancient times, the garden has been a place of beauty, creativity, energy and renewal. It has been a respite from the rush of everyday responsibilities. There we can center, finding harmony and balance with the natural elements. Our worries momentarily fade away and we are at peace.

Working in the garden gives us a special connection to nature. When we fully experience the warm earth flowing through our hands, the breeze brushing our cheeks and the smell of flowers tickling our nostrils, we intrinsically link with the universe.

Gardens created with plants indigenous to the area are particularly infused with the unique properties of the locality. These plants and trees are in their natural habitat. When the gardener understands and respects this, she is rewarded with vigorous growth and beauty. She connects with the land, nurtures it and fully benefits from its healing powers.

If we garden with enjoyment and with the intent to create beauty, inspiration rises from the depths of our hearts and souls. The garden evolves according to our own life's breath and natural flow. We create a sacred space for ourselves, our loved ones and for future generations that happen to come upon this special section of land. Our garden becomes a place where our own spirit connects with those of nature to provide a sacred space for all who enter. Our love will permeate their entire beings. They will find serenity and be renewed.

• Bringing Nature Indoors

If you live in a city and don't have a park nearby, you need not despair. You can still enjoy the benefits of connecting with nature. Put favorite plants and flowers in pots to be placed on balconies and in front of windows. Vibrant red geraniums are great plants for the novice gardener. They are hardy and forgiving. All they need is sunshine and regular watering to bloom in abundance.

Plants that do not require direct sunlight can be grouped around a favorite reading chair, on tables and even on the floor. Not only will you be creating lovely, tranquil havens in your home but you will also be helping to purify the atmosphere. African violets are popular indoor plants. Ferns provide a lushness that is soothing. Spring bulbs in forcing vases especially made for this purpose, can be placed in front of a sunny window, providing vivid, early seasonal color. Spend a few minutes every day centering, enjoying your creations of beauty and taking advantage of its healing forces.

Whether you go for outdoor walks, create a beautiful garden or tend pots of flowers indoors, your mind and body will soon respond to the rejuvenating powers of nature. You'll feel healthy and fit. Your spirits will soar and you will be at peace.

Chapter 11

The Serenity of Connecting With People

"Happiness . . . sharing kindness and compassion with others."
- - - The Dalai Lama

Independence has always been a desired trait in Western society. When Americans officially become adults at age eighteen, both they and their parents expect them to depart from the nest to pursue additional education or seek employment. Staying in the family home is often viewed as embarrassing and shameful. In fact, many young adults find themselves in schools or jobs a long distance from home, only spending time with their families on holidays and on rare special occasions.

Modern societies' transient tendencies have all but dismantled extended families. In more traditional cultures, relatives are available for support and comfort. Children become adults, marry and live close to their place of birth. Grandparents often live in the home of one of their adult children and provide wisdom and emotional support to both children and adults in the household. They also assist with child care. Other relatives are down the street or around the corner.

In the United States, the number of families without extended family support is increasing. We have more older adults in rest homes or assisted living facilities than does any other country in the world. We are succeeding in our desire to be individually self-sufficient. But, in our zeal to live independently, we are disregarding the value of family and social support. The extended family structure in America is increasingly viewed as unimportant. We are intensifying our isolation. For some people, the internet is the primary means of reaching out to others.

Sean's and Dan's Stories

In 1992, both Sean and Dan were diagnosed with Acquired Immunodeficiency Syndrome (AIDS). Both men were Caucasian males in their late twenties. Both had college degrees. Sean was a computer programmer; Dan, a financial planner. Both were avid readers and skilled sportsman participating in tennis, boating, skiing and hiking. Both began similar medical treatments at around the same time. Dan continues to live an active life marked only by occasional fatigue and the necessity of a daily regimen of a medicinal AIDS cocktail. Sean is dead.

Both men had similar backgrounds, education and interests. Why did one remain functional, living a relatively happy and productive life while the other weakened and died?

Medical researchers studying the cases have concluded that the one big difference between the two men was their support systems. When Dan's family and friends heard of his diagnosis, they rallied around him, providing love and care. They visited and encouraged him during rough times. When he regained enough strength to participate in activities, they accompanied him to movies, parties and on nature hikes. They went out for meals and provided continued camaraderie.

Sean, on the other hand was shunned by his family who was embarrassed by the disease and all that it implied. His friends moved on to other relationships leaving him to eventually live alone, in his weakening condition, in a small trailer on property owned by a compassionate woman. One friend from his former circle visited occasionally.

Having social support that is loving and compassionate is the best predictor of the recovery of good health. It's more powerful than any other health habits including diet and exercise. Our family and friends, who are our support system, play important roles in buffering the stresses in our lives. They help us face our concerns and diffuse our fears. When we have close relationships, there are fewer negative changes in the immune system. Risks for developing infectious diseases are lessened.

Unfortunately, isolation increases the risk of physical illness and psychological disorders. It can even lead to mortality. Being alone often antecedes sadness, depression and ultimately, susceptibility to diseases. Part of what keeps us physically and mentally stable is the knowledge that, in times of need, there are people we can approach to ask for help. It is healthier to rely on a family member who cares about us unconditionally then on a mere acquaintance.

If we don't live near family, it's important to develop good friends. When we have people to talk to we don't feel alone. We're no longer afraid. Fear comes from feeling that we are left by ourselves to face the unknown. When we share our feelings about a problem, concern or crisis, the interconnections with others can help keep us healthy and, if we are ill, can even help us heal faster.

The key to good mental and physical health through relationships is to treat others with kindness and compassion and to connect with people who view us in the same way. To be mutually supportive, relationships must be solidly built on affection, caring and respect. With this base of emotional security, we adopt a state of mind that is nonviolent, nonharmful and nonaggressive. We empathize with others and find their pain unbearable. We wish for them to be free of their suffering and feel a commitment and a responsibility to do what we can to lessen their misery.

Establishing a mutually supportive group of friends and family, one that we trust to always be there when we need them and who, we in turn, are available for, is the best medicine for health and healing.

Toxic People

However, not every relationship is affirming. All of us can think of someone with whom we would rather not be. Making connections with people indiscriminately for the sake of building a large group that we hope will be there when we need them does not foster peace of mind or good health. This is truly a case of quantity not being better than quality.

Marriage, the ultimate relationship, can promote physical and mental health but only if the affiliation is good. People who are married are generally healthier than those who are not. The following study supports this point, and although I am definitely not suggesting that this is justification for smokers to continue to smoke, I would like to share the interesting results of this research with you.

A 1967 Surgeon General's report on smoking and health compared age adjusted death rates for men who were cigarette smokers. The researchers found that those who smoked had twice the death rate of those that did not. However, when married smokers were compared with divorced non-smokers, the death rate was about the same. The men who were most at risk for cigarette-related deaths were smokers who were single, widowed or divorced.

Bad marriages can decrease the body's immune potential. They can raise stress levels to the point of chronicity and debilitation. Occasional conflict in a marriage is normal. Toxicity would depend on the frequency and the quality of the disagreements.

If there is daily conflict and hostility, the immune system remains at a heightened state of alertness. It has no opportunity to return to the state of equilibrium that is needed to keep the immune potential strong enough to meet both the everyday requirements of our bodies and to provide the needed energy to handle crises. We weaken and become ill.

The types of arguments that we have can also be a problem. Some verbalizations hurt deeply. There are things that people say to each other that break down the other person's self-esteem, wound them and leave them in a depressed state. Although this is generally not our intent, the targets of our wrath are reduced to conditions that render them unable to appropriately participate in the interaction. These verbal attacks, such as sarcasm, name-calling and insults, drain the strength of the recipients, often leaving them with decreased psychological stamina and reduced immune potential.

In healthier relationships, both people want the disagreement to end with a conclusion that is mutually acceptable. They want the conflict to be solved within the confines of love and respect.

In bad marriages, conflict becomes the arena in which one partner tries to build himself up by knocking the other person down. If she can chip away at her husband's self-esteem and destroy him bit by bit she will emerge victorious, renewed and vigorous. Unfortunately for the person who fights to destroy, happiness in a relationship doesn't come with "winning". It comes with treating partners with compassion and respect.

How do we recognize toxicity in ourselves and in others? Because it is generally easier to recognize the faults of the other person, we'll begin by discussing toxicity in people other than ourselves. Start by paying attention to how you feel around friends, family and acquaintances. Do you feel warm and supported when in their presence? Are you relaxed and open? Can you be yourself; are you comfortable revealing your truths? Or are you tense? Are you monitoring what you are saying and doing so as not to be annoying or irritating to the other person? Are you concerned that he will disapprove of who you really are?

Notice your own feelings toward others. Do you become instantly irritable when you are with a particular person? Do you find yourself being sarcastic and critical without apparent reason? Are you spending your time trying to think of something to say that will hurt her and, in turn, make yourself feel more powerful?

If you continually experience negative feelings in the presence of another, you are in a toxic relationship. This negativity can have a number of sources. You may have had repeated unhappy experiences with this person in which she was critical and sarcastic. Or it may be due to your own feelings of insecurity. You may feel that you're not smart enough, attractive enough or competent enough. Because of your own perceived opinion of someone as secure, competent and powerful, being with her may trigger your insecurities. Irregardless of the cause of your tension, taking a temporary break from being with this person can be helpful.

Step back and evaluate the relationship and decide what you can do to change it into a more positive one. You may decide that it is unsalvageable. Sadly, your ultimate choice may have to be to distance yourself from the people in your life that are toxic to you.

Developing Mutually Supportive Relationships

Good relationships increase our ability to maintain happiness and good health. Whether or not a person is alone with sadness is a major factor in determining if he will develop stress-related illnesses such as cardiovascular problems. The antidote to loneliness is love and concern. We all need someone to care about us and to truly listen to us when we speak. If interactions are warm and positive, the human connection is the most powerful healer. It is capable of neutralizing harmful influences on our bodies and our psyches.

True friendships are based on mutual trust and compassion. The development of true friendship begins with you and with me. With friendship comes responsibilities. We have a responsibility to suspend judgment and accept our friends as they are. If we want them to be different, we're not true friends; we're using them to meet an unfulfilled need of our own, one that festers deep within our own souls. It is a need that should be fulfilled on a personal level. But, when we're afraid to look at ourselves, it's easier to blame others.

We also have a responsibility to do them no harm. If we are thoughtlessly critical or self-serving, we owe our friends an apology. When we truly care, we treat them with respect.

We will also encourage their efforts and applaud their successes. When you are happy for others, sharing your joy increases vital life energy for both you and the people around you. This is important for good health.

The more we reach out to others with friendship and warmth, the more it comes back to us. There are many things that we can do to express our concern for other people. When we perform these acts of kindness, a warmth permeates our beings and extends to the people within our periphery. Those receiving our kindness become filled with good thoughts and feelings and they automatically extend this joy to others.

Gloria's Story

Gloria is an actress who moved to Los Angeles fifteen years ago, to pursue a career in movies. She was the first person in her family to move away from her hometown in Worthington, Minnesota. She left a large extended family support system along with friends whom she had known all her life.

Initially, Los Angeles was exciting. She loved the shows, theatres and dance clubs. There was always something to do; always the call for actors and actresses in the entertainment field. Although she was often hired for chorus work, for bit parts and for commercials, she had yet to get "the big break."

She eventually married her steady boyfriend whom she had been dating since moving to California. He was a scene locator; he traveled the world looking for the perfect locations for movies. His job often took him out of town.

Gloria continued to work until getting pregnant for the first time. Both she and her husband agreed that she would quit working to be at home with the baby. She loved her new avocation as wife and mother. Soon they had a second child. She still enjoyed what she was doing. The only downside was that her husband was often away and the responsibilities of the home and children were hers alone. When a child was ill, it was up to her to get him to the doctor's and make caretaking arrangements for her other child.

When she was tired, under-the-weather or just needing a break, there was no one to relieve her. At those times, she would call her mother just to hear a supportive voice.

One afternoon, she was buying diapers at her local drugstore. Her oldest child was in the stroller, the other in her arms. She met Maureen, a makeup artist who had worked with her on several commercials who was also shopping in the same aisle. As they chatted, Maureen mentioned that she also left her job to parent full time. She invited Gloria to join a play group. The group consisted of women with young children who got together once a week to socialize while their children played. The women also cared for each other's children and helped one another in times of need. Gloria soon became an integral part of the group. She no longer feels isolated and alone.

A postscript to Gloria's story: at this writing, the group is planning what they consider a daring adventure for women who are seldom without the responsibilities of their children. On a day when all of their husbands are in town, they'll leave their children in their husbands' care and drive to a spa in Newport Beach. They'll treat themselves to a well-deserved day of beauty treatments and relaxation in the company of good friends.

• Make Time To Be With Others

We're all so busy with juggling work and home responsibilities that we often don't take the time for rest and renewal. We don't get together often enough with friends to talk, laugh and take advantage of the healing power of the company of one another. However, our ability to perform at an optimum level requires that we regularly provide ourselves with the opportunity to regenerate. Being with people we care about is one of the quickest ways that we can replenish our physical and psychic energies.

Plan to get together with loved ones regularly. The gathering can be as simple as joining others for coffee and dessert or as elegant as a formal dinner. What's important is being with people with whom you can be open and honest; people you enjoy and are comfortable with in any situation.

Holidays are times that can be particularly difficult for people who are alone. Those who are isolated experience increased tension and loneliness, especially if they have had a recent loss. They could be at risk for a higher incidence of colds or the various strains of influenza. Reach out to your friends, especially those who are at risk, by inviting them to spend some time with you; to share some refreshment and companionship.

There are some guidelines to a successful gathering. Limit the size of the group. Six to eight people provide camaraderie and still allow a setting in which anyone who wants to share a thought is able to do so.

Linger. One cup of tea or coffee is good; two are better. Savor the repast. Bask in the warmth of friendship. When the time comes to part, you will go on your way filled with feelings of love and well-being.

• Be A Good Listener

Develop the art of listening. Everyone has the need to really be heard and most of us seldom are. If you become the kind of person who listens well, not only will you be sought out by your friends but you will experience the warmth that comes with a genuine connection with others.

Listening well means becoming the kind of listener that doesn't only hear but really listens. Let the speaker talk without offering opinions or advice. Listen with genuine interest, without judgment. Hear her happiness, her frustration, her pain. Be there for her and you may be surprised to realize that she is also there for you. She may not be there for you at that exact moment. Listening well means taking turns; allowing each other to talk until thoughts are completed, emotions are worked through.

• Smile Often

A smile is an immediate connection with others recognized by people throughout the world as an act of goodwill. When you smile with sincerity, it is an extension of the kindness and compassion that you are feeling toward your friends and acquaintances. It starts in your heart, moves to your mind and spreads through your whole being, finally bursting forth into the surrounding space. It is sensed by the people around you and enters their bodies and souls filling them with joy. They in turn, return that feeling to you and to others with whom they come in contact. Good feelings abound. Use your smile often. Spread happiness. You will be contributing to the well being of all humanity.

PART THREE

* * *

Paths To Recovery

Chapter 12

Recovery of Health

"Nature, time and patience are the three great physicians."
--- *H.G. Bohn*

Whenever we get sick, we assume that we'll get better; that the illness will run its course and we'll soon be as good as new. But what if we contract a disease that is potentially life-threatening such as cancer or coronary artery disease? Can we blithely assume a cure? Not at this point. However, medical scientists are continually researching that possibility for today's dreaded diseases. There have been advances in cancer medications and treatments. At one time, when a person was diagnosed with cancer, it was presumed that death was imminent. Because of modern medical discoveries, a patient now has a fifty-fifty chance of beating cancer and having it go into remission.

Recent discoveries regarding certain illnesses support that fact that lifestyle changes can retard and even reverse the course of many diseases. Coronary artery disease is one of them. We're learning that we can participate in the recovery of our health. We can adapt lifestyle habits and behaviors that provide the very best environment for cure.

Healing comes from within. It is our very nature as living organisms to move toward a return to equilibrium. Returning to health is a natural ability of the body. The incomparable value of the body's healing system is not its ability to produce remissions of disease but to maintain good health despite the menaces of daily life.

The concept of the placebo effect has earned a bad reputation among both the medical community and the general public. It has come to suggest that the illness is "all in the patient's mind" and that the symptoms are imagined. This may explain why certain people who report particular physical concerns experienced no symptoms after taking a "sugar pill" or a placebo, a substance that contained no properties known to fight the illness. The question to ponder is, "Could the symptom relief simply be the result of the body's natural curative powers performing its normal functions?"

The primary cause of illness is exposure to viruses. If our immune defenses are weakened, then a virus has an opportunity to play havoc with our bodies. There are three main categories of weakening influences on the immune system that impair our defenses: 1) persistent and overwhelming infections, 2) toxic injury by certain forms of matter and energy and 3) unhealthy mental states.

These factors cause problems that interfere with healing. Our breathing, which is vital to maintaining life, can be restricted. Our bodies need an adequate exchange of oxygen and carbon dioxide. If breathing is restricted, the body cannot perform this task to keep us well. Restrictions can be caused by physical traumas such as damage of the lungs and other important organs by smoking or living in an area in which we continually breathe toxins. It can also be caused by emotional stresses. When we are anxious or depressed, our breathing is short and shallow. We find ourselves gasping and gulping in an attempt to get more air. We don't do the normal deep abdominal breathing necessary for optimum functioning. If we have chronic anxiety, and shallow breathing becomes our usual method of respiration, our immune systems can be weakened to the point of vulnerability to illnesses and diseases.

The circulation of blood can be hampered by the weakening influences. Blood must circulate well to bring energy and healing materials to the malfunctioning or injured areas. Life choices such as poor diet, smoking and a sedentary lifestyle can interfere with good circulation.

The body may not get enough energy to function properly. Energy is supplied by metabolism, the process of converting caloric energy in food to chemical energy that the body can use for its various functions. Common reasons for insufficient metabolic energy are a depletion of energy by overwork, over-exertion and the lack of adequate rest and sleep. Whether or not we get enough metabolic energy is within our control. We can choose behaviors that keep our systems working well. We can choose to not smoke, to eat nutritious foods and to get regular exercise.

The healing system is responsible for the moment to moment maintenance of health. It also maintains the special functions required to manage injury and sickness. A coordinated interaction of stimulating and inhibiting factors affects the growth and proliferation of cells. The Chinese concept of balance and the Western concept of homeostasis refer to all factors working synchronically.

Practitioners of traditional Chinese Medicine talk about maintaining lifestyle behaviors that keep all systems in balance to insure good health. With illness, behaviors need to be altered to rebalance the systems.

Both Eastern and Western medical scientists agree that many components interact to provide the best mental and physical environment for healing. When each of these factors is fine-tuned and performing optimally, the possibilities of health recovery and longer life can be phenomenal. Many of the treatments will be administered and performed by your physician but there are things that you can do to actively participate in your health maintenance and recovery. We can't just expect our doctors to do it all. We also have a responsibility to do what we can to keep our immune systems strong.

Rest

Most important to healing is rest. Improving the quality of rest and sleep should be a top priority of people seeking to maintain good health and to heal. A good night's sleep is essential to a healing environment. It is during a period of rest, when all other systems are in a less active state, that the healing system can best do its work.

Common obstacles to sleeping well are noises and aches and pains. Ingesting stimulants earlier in the day and the inability to turn off one's mind also interferes with sleep.

•Noise

There are a number of ways to alleviate noise. Effective methods entail blocking out the distracting sound by something soothing and pleasant. Tapes and compact disks are available that provide white noise: ocean waves, birds twittering, a gentle wind. Soft, non-vocal music can also provide relaxation and lull us gently to sleep. I often use a recording of Tibetan singing bowls. The seductive tonal vibrations are most effective in distracting me from outside noises and transcending me to a quiet, peaceful state conducive to sleeping. They also synchronize with the vibrations of the heart to stimulate functioning energy.

•Aches and Pains

Oftentimes, aches and pains keep us tossing and turning all night in an attempt to find a position that will let us sleep. These discomforts can be reduced by spending several moments before bedtime relaxing. Five minutes of slow stretching is often enough to get the kinks out and leave us pain-free. Stretching the entire body is necessary. Concentrating on just the area of discomfort is often ineffective because the muscles are interconnected. A knot in one area can cause an ache in another. A warm bath before getting into bed does wonders in relieving tense muscles that may be causing discomfort. Light a candle. Add some aromatic bath salts. The essence of lavender evokes relaxation. You will quickly be in a sleep mode.

If you have a willing companion, have him or her give you a gentle massage. It doesn't have to be a lengthy, deep-muscle rub. It can be as simple as the application of lotion to the skin. This is wonderful for inducing sleep.

Aches and pains that continue for several nights should be reported to your doctor. If the cause of the pain is not due to a serious concern, a periodic visit to an osteopathic physician or a respected chiropractor could keep the body properly aligned and reduce chronic discomfort.

•Stimulants

When you feel tired, sluggish or drained of energy, your body is sending you a signal. You may be lacking energy-enhancing nutrients; you may need rest or exercise. You body is telling you to give it what it needs to return to it's optimum level of functioning.

In technologically-advanced societies, we often ignore our bodies when they tell us what is needed. Instead, we provide a temporary boost by ingesting a stimulant. Beverages such as coffee, tea, and colas contain caffeine that gives us a momentary lift but can interfere with sleep. Prescription and over-the-counter drugs include ingredients that can keep us awake. Street drugs such as cocaine and methamphetamines are sometimes used by people attempting to force more energy so they can do more work at a faster pace. Even if stimulants are taken early in day, they can have residual effects that interfere with a good night's sleep. They are best avoided.

We often disregard the message that our bodies are sending us about what it is lacking at the moment and use a stimulant to temporarily keep it going. If we continue to abuse our bodies in this way, they may eventually be unable to stand the strain. Organs will break down and not be able to do their part in our bodies' ability to function. A better way is to listen to what the body is saying about the need for renewal. Sleep is a time of rejuvenation.

•Turning Off The Mind

Whenever I have patients who report that they can't sleep and I ask them why, they most often report that they can't get past their thoughts and concerns. They lie in bed and try to ignore them but their minds are racing. Here are some techniques to calm a busy mind.

Write down the thoughts that are interfering with your sleep. This is most effective if done as the first thing in your bedtime preparation ritual. If you're already in bed, get out of bed to write. If you just lie there ruminating, your thoughts will keep you awake. Write down everything you're thinking. If you are having discord or a concern about another person, write your thoughts in the form of a letter to him or her. But ... a warning. Don't send the letter. You are free-writing; saying anything that comes into your head. Sharing your every thought in a written letter without editing it may damage your relationship. Free-writing at this time will allow you the opportunity to decide exactly what you want to say, at another time, in a way that will keep the friendship intact. It will also get thoughts out of your head so they will no longer keep you awake. You'll soon be relaxed enough to sleep.

Meditation also clears the mind so we can rest. Meditation techniques induce a state of "no thought" so this is ideal to free our minds from worries and concerns. A simple meditation was mentioned in chapter 5. Visualize your Qi, the source of energy according to the Chinese, in its house approximately two inches below your navel. Imagine that it's a small, warm ball of soft light the size of a Ping-Pong ball. Take three life-affirming, deep breaths. With the next breath, move your Qi through your body to the center of your forehead. As you slowly exhale, move your Qi back along the same route, and return it to its house. Breathe in again and move your Qi to your forehead. Breathe out as you return your Qi back to its house. Continue doing this as you become more and more relaxed. If thoughts enter your mind, sweep them away and focus on moving your Qi. You'll soon be asleep.

Exercise

Exercise is vital to getting all the body's systems to function at their level of peak performance. It improves circulation. It increases the heart's ability to pump blood quickly and smoothly through the arteries, keeping those arteries open and free from impediments. It enhances the work of the respiratory system, facilitating the exchange of oxygen and carbon dioxide. It assists elimination by increasing the flow of perspiration and the movements of the intestines. It regulates metabolism, improves mood and reduces stress. It strengthens the immune system.

Choose activities that you enjoy. Many people walk for their exercise but there are other activities for your selection. Pursuits such as gardening, fishing, or wandering through an open-air bazaar provide mild but steady movement. Jogging, tennis or bicycling render more strenuous exertion. What ever you choose, do something to get your body moving everyday. Not only will it lift your mood, but you'll be helping to keep your body in good working order.

If you're recovering from an illness, start slowly with a short walk in your yard or around your house and then progress to more vigorous activities as your energy level and your doctor permits. Monitor your body. Don't push yourself to detrimental levels. Rest when your body tells you it's time to do so.

Nutrition

Healing requires energy. Energy is supplied by metabolism, the process of converting caloric energy in food to chemical energy that the body can use for its various functions. The key to eating for health maintenance and recovery is choosing the kinds of foods that supply energy for good health and avoiding foods that gunk up the system or provide meaningless calories. Avoid being overweight or overly thin by eating in moderation. Make the bulk of your food choices a wide variety of fruits, vegetables, grains and legumes. The rest of your food should come from low or non-fat dairy products, fish, poultry and lean meats.

The United States Department of Agriculture (USDA) outlines its recommendations in the form of a pyramid with fruits, vegetables and grains at the bottom of the pyramid and sugar products at the small area of the apex. This guideline is good to keep in mind whether you are maintaining or recovering health. Improving your diet is one of the major changes you can make to decrease your health risks. If your particular illness requires specific dietary needs (for example, low salt intake for people with coronary disease) your doctor will discuss this with you. In any event, ask your physician about particular food choices or restrictions that would assist in your healing.

Two excellent source books on eating to facilitate the healing process are *Eating Well For Optimum Health* by Andrew Weil, M.D. and *Reversing Heart Disease* by Dean Ornish, M.D.

Thoughts, Beliefs and Emotions

What do you think about your illness? Do you belief that because of the kind of disease you have you will die? Are you so depressed that you lie around all day, still in your pajamas, and stare into space or at the television screen? Your thoughts, beliefs and emotions influence your behavior, what you choose to do, how you interact with others. They greatly influence your body's ability to heal.

•Thoughts

It's normal to worry about your health when you're ill. With a long-term illness or a life-threatening disease, it would be easy to think about your condition all the time and to be constantly monitoring your body for pain and discomfort. To help ease your mind, take the following steps.

Get your affairs in order. When people think of preparing for a debilitating illness or condition or even death, they often avoid by saying, "I'll do it tomorrow when I have more time." Tomorrow becomes tomorrow which becomes tomorrow. To avoid confusion among your loved ones and to settle your affairs in the way you want, do it today. Don't put off preparing a will. Talk to someone about any special desires that you have. This will prevent chaos in the event that you reach a point where you're unable to verbalize what you want.

Follow your doctor's orders. Comply with recommendations of treatment. Take your medications. He is there to help you improve and heal.

Stick to your daily routine of exercise, good nutrition, and a stress-reducing activity to promote serenity. Be attuned to what your body is telling you. Rest when you need to. One of the major reasons for obsessive thoughts is guilt over not doing the things we should do. If a fifteen minute walk is on your daily "to do" list, you will experience pangs of guilt if you decide not to do it. Just do it. If you do, you will be guilt-free and have a feeling of accomplishment.

If you follow these three steps then you know that you've done everything that you can do. All else is in the hands of fate. You can relax, savor each moment and leave the outcome to a higher being.

Optimism plays a key role in maintaining health. How do you interpret life and the things that happen to you?

John's and Jim's Stories

John and Jim were both passed over for a promotion. John is disappointed but not crushed by the decision. His attitude is, "Oh well. It's just a bad break. Maybe next time." Jim is devastated and wonders what is wrong with him. "I'm so stupid. The management team doesn't think I have what it takes to do the job and I probably don't. I'll never be successful at anything."

John's interpretation is that circumstances at that time were just not right for him and there will other opportunities for advancement. Jim views himself as inept.

The management's decision to not give him the higher position confirms, to him, his feelings of overall unworthiness.

Research supports the premise that pessimism may adversely affect the immune system. Pessimistic people may feel that they are under greater stress. Those thoughts actually increase their stress levels and could interfere with their immune functioning. They become vulnerable to illness and disease.

•Beliefs

What you believe can influence the healing process. If you believe that you can improve your condition by performing certain activities, you are more likely to stick to your regimen than a person who is unsure that those activities will aid his ability to influence recovery.

The belief system has yet a more esoteric affect. The power of the mind has been demonstrated in the placebo phenomenon. Studies show that if a person believes that she is taking a pill to cure certain ailments such as hypertension when she is really taking a sugar pill, it is likely that her blood pressure level will drop.

Belief in your physician is also important to healing. If you trust that your physician is skilled and has your best interest at heart, you are more likely to comply with his medical advice and treatment schedule.

• Emotions

There is no direct, absolute connection between emotions and illness. Some people identified as a particular personality type will get certain illnesses while others will not. However, theories have developed that describe personalities which are prone to certain illnesses. Remember that other factors must be taken into consideration. These include genetic and environmental predispositions and health-related habits or detriments including smoking, drinking alcohol in excess and poor dietary choices.

An example of a possible personality-related illness is coronary heart disease. It seems to be especially common among people who have hostile and angry personalities. These are people who over-react to mild and moderate stresses and have difficulty regrouping.

Character traits such as depression, anxiety, anger and hostility appear to raise the overall risk of disease. Modifying these traits by learning to perceive the world's challenges differently can help you to be stress-hardy. If we adapt a more positive attitude we may be able to weaken our body's relationship between stress and disease.

The passionate desire to be healthy again and a positive attitude that one can do things to assist the body in moving toward a desired outcome, are important intellections that influence the healing process.

Serenity

Take time every day to participate in an activity that results in feelings of serenity. When you are calm and serene your immune system is free to work at its optimum level and to help you heal. Serenity releases your natural healer, the part of you that puts your systems in perfect balance. It regulates the flow of blood, the immune system and the killer T-cells so that they are in perfect harmony to work their wonders. It allows the healing properties to overcome obstructions and keep your Qi flowing smoothly. It is the quintessential condition for healing.

Partnering With Your Physician

When doctors treat someone for a specific illness, they not only prescribe antibiotics for that illness, but they also check to make sure that the patient's underlying physical condition is such that he can take and tolerate the medications. As long as there is adequate physical strength, there is the potential within to make use of the medications to heal.

Cure is generated by the body's healing system. Treatment, including drugs and surgery, can remove obstacles and facilitate healing. Antibiotics can reduce the destructive effects of the invading germs. Still, treatment is not synonymous with healing. Treatment originates outside of you; healing comes from within. However, refusing treatment while waiting for cure can be most unwise.

Your physicians are the health providers who are experts in determining your health requirements. They supply medical skill along with information about the newest medicines, methods and technology. You, as the patient, contribute a body that is increasingly conducive to healing. Together, you provide the ultimate partnership for health recovery.

Chapter 13

Living In The Moment

"Cat lies in the sun. Turtle basks on the rock.
Man sits in the garden. All creatures ... in the moment."

- - - Liu Kum Sung

Every day, Marnie rises in the coolness of the early morning. It's a perfect moment. Her husband and children are still asleep and the time is hers and hers alone. She makes a cup of coffee and takes it into the back yard. The morning is dawning in a blue haze. The moon is fading into the firmament. She eases into a comfortable old wicker chair with cushions that, over the years, have developed an imprint that molds to her body. She tucks her feet under her and slowly sips her coffee. She is suspended in that delicious time of wakening between gentle sleep and full awareness. Her mind is free from thought allowing her to meld with the purlieu of the breaking day. The birds are singing, tiny butterflies are flitting from bush to bush. A soft breeze touches her cheek. She sits sipping her coffee, savoring this time of tranquillity.

Essential to reaping the benefits of serenity's healing force is the ability to be in the present moment; to center and block out both internal and external distractions. This focus on the here-and-now is called mindfulness by Western advocates and centering by teachers and practitioners of Qigong. It is using all of your senses to experience the present moment. It promotes feelings of calm, serenity and well-being.

When we are obsessed with troublesome thoughts they generally have nothing to do with the present moment. They are most often about another time. Ruminating about past mistakes and what one might have done differently has no value and can lead to depression. Worrying about future events can trigger anxiety. Depression and anxiety are detrimental to the psyche. They deplete energy needed to keep the body's functions working smoothly. They also suppress the immune potential.

Both Eastern and Western practitioners agree that proper breathing is necessary to move from attention on everyday thoughts and concerns to a place of mindfulness. It is the key to shifting consciousness and moving into this early stage of meditativeness. Buddhist monks often refer to this as spaciousness. They talk of being spacious to increase awareness and to move closer to enlightenment.

Diaphragmatic, therapeutic breathing is the type of breathing that allows you to enter the mindful state. Breathe slowly. On each in-breath, expand your belly. On the out-breaths, relax and let your belly deflate. After breathing this way for a few minutes you will be in a mindful state. Your mind will be focused within. Your concentration will be on the moment. Your inner healer will be free to do its work. Your life energy, the Qi, will be stimulated to keep you well-functioning and to help you heal.

In their book, *The Power of the Mind to Heal*, Joan and Miroslav Borysenko mention a more advanced type of breathing called "the breath of bridging earth and heaven." This is best done outdoors where you can connect with all the powers of nature.

Sit or stand outdoors. Begin taking slow, diaphragmatic breaths. Close your eyes. Continue to breathe. When you're comfortable, with your next in-breath, breathe in the powers of the heavens. Allow them to enter your body through the top of your head. Let them flow into your heart. With each out-breathe, exhale your essences and let them mingle with those of the heavens. Continue to breathe in the powers of the heavens and breathe out your essences.

When you're ready, along with commingling your energies with the energies of the heavens, take in the powers of the earth through your feet. With each in-breathe you are now taking in the energies of both the heavens and the earth.

Allow them to flow to your heart and swirl together also incorporating your essences. On an out-breath send this mixture out of your body into the universe.

Now open your eyes and survey nature all around you. As you continue to breathe, you connect with the power of all living things. With each breath, you nurture the universe as it nurtures you.

You can use therapeutic breathing to stay in the moment. You can also use it to induce a state of calmness whenever you are frustrated or stressed. Use it when you are in a long supermarket line or stuck in traffic. As you breathe, you will feel your tension level decrease.

Major stressors such as concern for an elderly parent with dementia or an illness of your own, require a deeper meditation, on a regular basis, so you have the fortitude to handle the situation. A deeper meditation is necessary to relieve the anxiety or depression that could become debilitating or cause you to make impulsive decisions that may not be the best ones. Then you can use "the breath of bridging earth and heaven."

Many people see mindfulness as a condition that requires a quiet place. However, throughout the day most of us have here-and-now experiences. They happen whenever we are comfortably absorbed in what we're doing; when we're doing something with full attention. It is that moment of complete concentration when we are participating fully. Our activity becomes effortless. We perform with precision. Athletes refer to it as being "in the zone." Writers and artists call it being "in the flow." A cultural teaching of the Chinese is that this spacious state is one that we should strive for in our daily endeavors. It is also the best condition for healing.

This is the moment of launching
All auspicious signs are aligned

PART FOUR

***

Charting Your Personal Course

Chapter 14

Healing Your Soul

"Your pain is the breaking of the shell that encloses understanding."
- - - Kahlil Gabran

If you have been diagnosed with a serious illness, particularly one that is life-threatening, you remember being shocked and bewildered when your doctor confirmed your problem. You didn't believe that it was happening to you. You were disoriented and confused. It was difficult to concentrate or focus your attention. You had mood swings. At times you were depressed. At other times you felt near panic. You felt as if you were nothing but an empty shell of swirling emotions.

However, the initial period of shock passes. The intensity of feelings decreases and drops to a more manageable level. As your physicians provide medical treatment and care, your ability to be serene, to set up a perfect milieu for the possibility of cure, is all important. "But how can I be serene at a time like this?" you ask. "I'm frightened. All I seem to do is worry. I'm worried about the future. I don't want to die. There are things I haven't done. Unfinished projects. Problems that still need to be resolved."

Health professionals agree that there is no one absolute state of mind that correlates with the activation of the healing system. However, it appears that accepting the disease often obtains a better result than railing against it. Acceptance of the disease doesn't mean giving up hope for more time on earth than prognosis predicts. It doesn't mean becoming depressed, withdrawing from the world and the people and activities that you love. It means acknowledging the illness.

Some people, unconsciously, prefer to ignore their own illnesses. The negative messages they've received and the traumas they've experienced since childhood have caused them to turn a deaf ear to their reality. They avoid the true unencumbered voice of their own soul. Because they disavow the illness, they don't participate in healing.

The ability to accept one's reality with grace is a part of a larger acceptance of self. When we are comfortable with ourselves and all that we are and have been, we move toward peace, calmness and serenity.

What you learn in this chapter will help you heal your soul. It will improve the quality of the rest of your life. We can transcend suffering. We can learn and grow. What we cannot be guaranteed is physical cure. However, we can insure that our remaining days are serene. Once we've faced our fears, we can go on to live the rest of our lives, not only despite them, but in a fuller and more present way, because of them.

Taking Care of Unfinished Business

Most of us have unfinished business that keeps us tense and agitated. Healing our souls involves opening our hearts and dealing with these issues. This begins, first of all, with accepting who we really are. Allow yourself to dig deep down into your soul. If you've been having difficulty looking at yourself throughout your life, you will discover that you really do have the courage to face your true reality. This means coming to terms with disappointments and regrets you've experienced; resolving hurtful and hostile relationships. We also need to examine our beliefs about the purpose of life and death and what happens in the hereafter. Until we deal with these issues, peace will elude us.

Acceptance of Self

Healing of the soul can sometimes lead to physical cure. Being able to accept ourselves is an integral part of this process. Irregardless of whether we get our wish of complete cure, physical recovery cannot even begin to occur unless we acknowledge our constricted natures and work diligently to break down the barriers that are hampering our abilities to discover and accept who we are.

Carl Jung, a pioneer in human behavior theory, talked about the persona we take on and the masks we wear to win approval from others. By the time we're adults, we have assumed many different roles. Some are appropriate and helpful to us - the good mother, the supportive wife, but some are taken on to please others - the quiet and always compliant son, the subservient employee - and may be accompanied by expectations that we resent. When we are authentic, being who we really are, we go forth with confidence, open-heartedness and compassion. When we hide our true selves behind masks, we are tense, anxious, irritable, resentful. Our discomfort shows. People sense our agitation and react toward us with suspicion and distrust. The process of becoming our true selves requires disgarding the masks that we have donned to please others and to hide the parts of us that they have said are unacceptable. We resent these masks. Our anger escalates when we think we have to put them on.

According to Buddhist thought, there are three poisons of the mind that keep us from being ourselves and finding peace: 1) ignorance of the true nature of ourselves and thus, the inability to accept who we are, 2) abject craving and 3) unrelenting hatred. By having awareness of our inner selves, being the kind of person we can love and respect, and by eliminating craving and hatred, there is freedom from emotional suffering.

Resolving Disappointments and Regrets

Hostile and negative emotions such as anger, resentment, criticalness, hopeless resignation and debilitating disappointment block our ability to develop tranquillity. Healing the soul involves getting rid of these negative states of mind and cultivating the positive states of kindness, compassion, love and tolerance. This letting go of negative emotions is at the very heart of physical, emotional and spiritual healing. For many people, it may be the catalyst to physical cure from disease and ailments. Achieving a sense of peace and spiritual strengthens the body, enabling us to handle the side effects of whatever medical treatment we're undergoing and advance the process of healing both emotionally and immunologically.

Negative emotions automatically occur as a reaction to an adverse situation or a person who hurts us. This is natural and normal. What is debilitating is not resolving the conflict for ourselves and holding on to the emotion past the period of appropriateness. When we feel that someone has hurt our feelings and we feel anger and resentment long after the incident, we have not come to resolution. This hinders our ability to heal.

Also interfering with obtaining serenity are feelings of guilt. Guilt arises when we think we have made an irreparable mistake; in thinking that problems are permanent because of our actions. However, we could try to view things differently. Difficult circumstances and negative emotions can be raw materials for the growth of our souls. According to the Dalai Lama, "If there is a solution to the problem, there is no need to worry. If there is no solution, there is no sense in worrying either." He also teaches that change is inevitable. "At any given moment, no matter how pleasurable - or how difficult - a moment may be, it will not last." Do not regret the change that occurs. In a difficult situation, realize that this too will pass.

To reduce anxiety, change the motivation of your actions. Be sincere. Do your best with kindness and compassion. Then, even if you fail or make a mistake, there's no cause for regret. Remind yourself that you're doing your best. If you're unsuccessful, it's because the situation is beyond your best efforts. When your motivation is sincere, it dissolves fear and builds feelings of self-worth. Anxiety increases when your motivation is selfish and self-serving.

Relationships

In the rush of our daily lives, it's easy to look outside of ourselves for the reasons that we are tense and irritable. We often point to other people as the reason for our frustrations. The traffic is snarled because other drivers are rude. They don't know the basic rules of driving safely. The supermarket line is long and slow-moving because the check- out clerk isn't concentrating on what she's suppose to do. Not only is she slow, but she laughs and socializes with each customer and other employees when she should be paying more attention to checking people out. The most irritating situations are those that we can't mold to our liking.

At these times, the best solution is within ourselves. We can take deep, healing breaths, focus our attention within and replace anger and irritation with caring and understanding. As we breathe deeply, we can give ourselves alternate messages. The people in the other cars also had a long day and are anxious to get home. We're all in the same boat. By laughing and talking to others, the supermarket clerk is spreading joy and providing camaraderie. As we deep breathe, we can listen to the laughter and enjoy the warmth that it brings.

We can learn to alter our mental state. If we're tempted to insult someone or yell at a person who has inconvenienced us, we can refrain from doing so by taking healing breaths and searching for the good or the commonality in the situation. We can look within ourselves for kindness and understanding. We can have a healing moment.

More difficult to deal with than people we encounter every day are resentments that are ongoing or unfinished from the past. They gnaw at us. Whenever, we think of a particular incident or person who has offended us, we relive that scenario and actually feel the emotions connected to the incident over and over and over again. What about those?

Both Eastern and Western healers of psychic and emotional pain talk about forgiveness. The Dalai Lama talks about forgiving people who have hurt us and replacing the anger and resentment with kindness and compassion. "That's easier said than done," you say. You're right, but there are some things you can do to help rid yourself of negative emotions evoked by past resentments. You will then find true peace and serenity.

Joan and Milo Borysenko in their book *The Power Of The Mind To Heal*, state that forgiveness is not apologizing and making amends. It is resolving the situation for yourself.

Your goal is to eventually think of the person or incident without emotionality; without hurting all over again. You may choose never to see him again; to eliminate him from your life. That's fine. What you want to do is truly separate yourself by breaking your emotional attachment. You want to enter the mental space where thinking of the person does not evoke hurtful, angry feelings. This emotional state is one of neutrality, where your own negative emotions are not triggered. It is a psychic place where you can view the other person with a bit of understanding.

The Borysenkos discuss steps to forgiveness. A good way to begin to reduce your feelings is to write about them. Write about your thoughts and feelings at each of the following steps until the feelings begin to subside. This may take several writing sessions of addressing the same issues. Then go on to the next step. Don't edit or judge what you've written. Just write.

1) Grieve for what has been lost. Express your disappointment in

what you had hoped the relationship would have been. Acknowledge that because of the other person's actions or demands, he or she is not the kind of person that you respect or admire; that you would not choose him or her for a friend. If you feel that the person has taken something from you or deprived you of something that was rightfully yours, admit your sorrow over the loss. Grieve.

2) Express your anger about the person or situation.

3) Accept the loss. What is done is done.

4) Come to resolution through understanding. What have you learned about the other person? His motivation? His character? His personal unmet needs and how he tries to get them met? What have you learned about yourself? As you develop understanding, your resentment will subside.

Make peace of mind your goal. The way toward a life of tranquillity and serenity is through forgiveness. Healing our hurtful relationships is a letting go, not a hanging on. Healing is a series of deaths and rebirths. As we put resentment and fear to death we are reborn with a greater capacity for understanding and love. We strengthen our basic spiritual qualities of goodness, kindness, compassion and caring. These qualities are essential to our physical and emotional well-being and that of greater mankind.

Life, Death and The Hereafter

Life

One of the questions that we struggle with periodically throughout our existence is "What is the meaning of life?" As we read works of the great thinkers and philosophers in both Eastern and Western societies we find tomes of ideas and thoughts expressed in different ways. They all come down to one basic premise. The Dalai Lama states it succinctly. "To seek happiness." People agree that happiness is feelings of joy, tranquillity and optimism.

Jim's Story

Jim is a 38-year-old married man with three young children. He has a college degree and is in middle management in a fiber optics company. His wife is a stay-at-home mom. His day ends when he returns to a hot meal, a comfortable home and a loving family. Still, he often feels restless and unfulfilled so he was excited when he received an unexpected windfall. A favorite aunt died and left him enough money to live comfortably without working. He decided not to give up his job but to cut his hours to part time.

He began to spend more time with his family and took them on fabulous vacations. He bought things he wanted but never felt he could afford. A ski boat. A cashmere top coat. After a year he admitted to a good friend, "You know, I'm still not really happy."

Jade's Story

Jade was diagnosed with esophageal cancer. She endured several years of radiation, chemotherapy and surgery. Still weak and thin but in her second year of remission she said, "This has been tough but I'm happy. I am so thrilled to see each new day. It's exciting to hear the birds sing, to feel the breeze, to sit with my friends. My illness has given me a whole new perspective in appreciating every moment."

Happiness is determined more by a person's state of mind than by external events. Large segments of society have mistakenly determined that happiness is acquisition. They attempt to mask anxiety and unhappiness by acquiring things: new cars, fashionable clothes, bigger houses. They also numb nervousness or negative feelings by smoking, drinking alcohol, eating in excess and taking prescription, over-the-counter and street drugs. All these attempts provide either an immediate, temporary high or a sense of calm depending on the method chosen for coping. But when the effects wear off, the tension returns. More of what is being used to mask unhappiness is needed: another cigarette, another drink, more clothes, a still bigger house.

Only by realizing that happiness comes from within can we ever find true joy. By bringing about a certain inner discipline, we can change our attitudes and our entire outlook and approach to living. We can also change our behaviors.

Some people see the search for individual happiness as selfish and self-centered. They are wrong. As we find true happiness and peace within ourselves we become more positive, more creative and more flexible. We are more sociable and caring for others. We become more altruistic and find ourselves reaching out to others when they need our comforting. The closer we get to being motivated by altruism, the more fearless we become in the face of even extreme anxiety-provoking circumstances.

We're better able to tolerate life's daily frustrations than are unhappy people. Unhappy people are self-focused, brooding, critical and antagonistic. They're resentful, mean and hostile.

They tend to act out aggressively in word or in deed. They're quick to blame others for their unhappiness.

Learning to look within, emerge ourselves in our peaceful center and view others with kindness, compassion and true understanding produces an inner well-spring of joy. It is the key to happiness. It reduces stress and enhances immune functioning.

Death

Death is a part of existence. We're all going to die. The only question is "When?"

With a life-threatening illness, the likelihood that death could be imminent is a reality. People with cancer or heart disease realize that death from the illness is a definite possibility . Dying is often on their minds during the course of the illness. Often, they'd like to talk about it. Families of patients generally find death more difficult to address than do the patients themselves. If that's the case, the patient may choose not to bring it up so not to upset his loved ones. In not talking about it, he doesn't resolve his own concerns. Coming to terms with death would give him peace and serenity.

When we choose to do so, we should be allowed and even encouraged to examine our views of dying. We have a right to take charge of our dying as well as how we live our lives and our last days. Confronting our fears and beliefs about death relieves anxiety. It also reduces some of the physical pain that can come with dying. We can discuss our thoughts and feelings with our family, a close friend or a spiritual leader. The decision that a person must ultimately make is, does she struggle to regain good health or is it time to move on. Whatever the decision, family, friends and doctors need to respect the patient's choice and be supportive of the process.

Doctors working with patients who have terminal illnesses report that the patients seem to intuitively realize when it's time to let go. Whether or not a patient recovers from his illness or passes on, by participating in his treatment, resolving unfinished business and relishing every remaining day, he will have succeeded in improving the quality of his living and of his dying.

By orchestrating his last days, deciding whether he wants to be at home instead of in the hospital, selecting things and people he wants around him, he can pass on in comfort. A perfect ending to life for many people is to have soft music playing while dying. Favorite musical selections can be deeply soothing to the patient and to his loved ones. Physical pain decreases. His mind is at rest. Death comes peacefully.

Buddhist philosophy advocates "healing into death," ultimately viewing our lives as complete and accepting the disintegration of the physical body.

We prepare for whatever comes after death according to our own beliefs. Conceptions about what happens is dictated by the spiritual, religious and cultural teachings that have influenced us. The early Taoist philosopher, Chuang Tze (approximate dates: 369 to 286 BC), states that death is no more than the necessary and proper correlative of human life. It is rest from work, freedom from illness.

We pass over to a place of inspiration and intuition. A place that transcends time, space and matter. We become part of something which is greater than physical existence. We take the next step in the eternal process of cosmic change.

When we resolve our unfinished issues, solidify our beliefs and prepare for whatever comes next, we can face the future without concern. We have acquired a sense of calm and serenity. We are providing our immune system with the best possible environment to do its work. Our time on earth may be prolonged. We have healed our souls.

Chapter 15

Finding Your Healing Force

"A merry heart doeth good like medicine."
— — — *Proverbs XVII.22*

You're walking along a mountain path. The air is cool. The sun is filtered by tall trees. You hear the sound of birds and the rustling of leaves. Suddenly you notice a clearing ahead. As you approach you realize that it's a small meadow. At the far side of the grassy expanse, standing amidst some wildflowers, are a doe and her fawn. You stop, remaining absolutely still, and watch in awe. A warmth flows through your entire body. Your mood is elevated. You experience total emotional and physical well-being.

You have just had a healing moment, one perfect moment when all body systems are optimally functioning. The experience is both physical and spiritual. These are the moments of absolute pleasure best described as a warmth that permeates your body and elevates your mood. They are specific to each person. For some people, they can be triggered by a hug from a beloved friend or family member. For others, it can simply be the act of caressing a smooth wood carving. Still others experience the sensation when standing on a mountain top in a blowing wind.

Joan Borysenko, PhD, a medical scientist and author of books on health and healing, calls them holy moments. According to Dr. Borysenko, these moments are the doorways where *chronos* - linear clock time, meets *kairos* - eternal timelessness. These are the times when curing can sometimes occur - both through physical pathways and through a grace that transcends the physical.

In these moments, a person's heart opens and the life energy, which the Chinese refer to as Qi, is stimulated. Qi is activated and is dispersed throughout the body. The feeling can well up within us when we're with people we love and who love us. It is often evoked when we are connected with nature. It is particularly powerful in sacred places.

It's difficult to describe what is happening in that moment. It's a phenomenon that is better experienced than put into words. People throughout the ages have tried to describe it. Medical scientists have attempted to verbalize what is happening physiologically. Although different words and phrases have been used to describe the experience, a review of the literature shows that there are common themes. It has been described as a momentary spell or trance, a sense of harmony with all of the universe that enters and surrounds our beings. We enter an exalted zone of transcendence. In this shift of experience we spiral inward to make contact with our healing energies. We reach into the source of healing and regeneration that is a magic well that replenishes itself endlessly. The underlying energy source within us that infuses all of life is stimulated. At that healing moment we are in a state of optimal healing potential.

Christiane Northrup, MD is co-founder of Women to Women, a health care center in Yarmouth, Maine and assistant clinical professor of Obstetrics and Gynecology at the University of Vermont School of Medicine. She suggests a visualization that triggers both the sympathetic and the parasympathetic nervous systems to produce a healing moment.

Put your hand on your heart. Take a deep, healing breath. Think of someone you love, unconditionally. (A child or a pet is ideal. Adults are hard to use.) Enjoy the overwhelming good feeling.

When these healing times occur for you, pause, breathe deeply and experience the moment. Having three to five healing moments per day, in which your healing force is activated, contributes to the maintenance of health and the healing of the soul.

Chapter 16

Six Weeks to Better Health

"To be what we are ... to become what we are capable of becoming."
Robert Louis Stevenson

I have taken the information in this book and devised a six-week plan that you can use to refine your daily lifestyle to strengthen your immune system. Faithfully follow the regimen you've selected for six weeks. If you do, your lifestyle changes will become habits and you'll find it easy to continue on with your new daily routine to maintain your health or to assist in your physical healing if you are ill.

Eliminate the use of substances that weaken your immune system. If you smoke, enter a smoke cessation program to rid your body of this toxin. If you use street drugs and alcohol and find that you cannot stop usage without assistance, enter a drug and/or alcohol program. Breaking these habits and removing them from your lifestyle will go a long way in strengthening your immune potential. You will be on your way to healthy living.

WEEK ONE

Diet Evaluate your eating habits. Make the bulk of your food intake fruits, vegetables and grains. Eat five vegetables and three to five fruits every day. Eliminate red meat. Eat fish and skinless chicken and turkey in moderation. Reduce your intake of sugar.

Exercise Move! A brisk walk - five to seven days a week - is ideal. Your goal is to walk for thirty minutes. If you have difficulty with walking for this length of time, start with five minutes. A five-minute walk seven days a week will get you going.

Walk for one minute. Stop and do some slow stretches. Reach your arms and hands to the sky. Hold for five seconds. Relax. Bend slowly from the waist and reach to the ground. Try to touch your toes. Hang there gently for five seconds. Return to a standing position. With hands on your waist, twist to the left to the count of five, then twist to the right. After your stretches to keep yourself limber and improve your flexibility, resume your walk for an additional four minutes.

Therapeutic Breathing Practice healing breaths every day. Each session should last for twenty minutes for maximum results. You may use meditation techniques mentioned in this book or one that you have learned from another source. There are some important rules. Keep the method simple so you don't have to refer to directions while practicing. Use the same exercise for the entire six weeks (repetition is important to develop a habit and to keep the mind clear from thought.) Push out any thoughts that may enter your head. Then return your attention to your breathing task. Two simple techniques are : 1) paying attention to the breath and 2) moving the Qi.

•Paying Attention To The Breath

Sit or lie in a quiet, comfortable place. Put your tongue on the ridge between your gums and your upper front teeth. Start taking slow, deep breaths. When you're ready, pay attention to your breaths. Experience the air entering your body as you inhale. Feel the air leaving your body as you exhale. Notice your abdomen rising and falling. If you feel tense in any part of your body, relax that area and let the tension go. Take your attention back to your breathing. Continue for twenty minutes.

• Moving The Qi

This exercise is Meditation 2 in the chapter on meditation. Refer to the discussion that you will find there. Remember to put your tongue on the ridge between your gums and your upper front teeth. Start taking slow, deep breaths. When you're ready, move your Qi as described in Chapter 5.

Heal Your Soul Do a daily activity to heal your soul. Resolving unfinished business or past hurts are necessary to creating a good physical environment for healing. You can journal for 15 minutes or spend time with a friend or support group. If you choose to be with a friend, make sure this is someone who agrees to take this time to be there for you. His or her task is to just listen to you. This is not the time to participate in reciprocal conversation or for you to listen to him. That's for another time.

This activity can be varied. You can journal on one day, visit with a friend on another and meet with a support group on still another.

Serenity Participate in an activity that provides serenity two or three times a week. Remember to focus your attention on what you are doing and the pleasurable feelings that come with it. Be in the moment. Push away interfering thoughts. My favorite activities are sitting on my recliner and listening to quiet non-vocal music, writing poetry and walking along the shore of the ocean or a lake. Choosing different activities from day to day provides interest and unexpected delights.

WEEK TWO

<u>Diet</u> Continue with the plan started in week one. To get the most benefit from the vitamins and minerals in fruits and vegetables eat as many different kinds as possible. Continue to restrict your intake of fats and salt. Minimize red meat.

<u>Exercise</u> If you started your exercise program with a daily five-minute walk, extend it to ten minutes. Walk for two minutes and then stop to stretch. Walk for an additional eight minutes. If you are an experienced walker and are comfortable walking briskly for twenty minutes, you may want to try other exercise activities. You might take a class in Taijiquan or Yoga, go on a bike ride or for a swim. If you take a class, the instructor will advise you to participate within your capabilities. You can stop when you get tired or need to rest. Experience the joy of movement.

<u>Therapeutic Breathing</u> Continue with your chosen breathing activity. Remember that continuity and repetition is important; therefore, use the same breathing exercise you chose during week 1.

<u>Heal Your Soul</u> Journal for 15 minutes. Choosing the same time every day makes it part of your daily routine. My husband gets up early and journals at 5 AM. I like to write just before bed. I sit in front of the fireplace and scribble my thoughts, feelings and happenings of the day. This is a great way to get any concerns or worries that I may have, out of my mind. It allows me to sleep soundly. On days that you are not journaling, visit with a friend.

<u>Serenity</u>   One day this week, visit a favorite museum. Do this alone. If you have always visited museums with a companion, you will be surprised at the new awareness that you will get being alone. Wander, pausing at paintings, sculptures and other objects d'arte that evoke an emotion. If the feeling is particularly strong, spend more time there. The object or painting is helping you reach down into the inner place in your body where healing originates. Sit. Let go of your thoughts. Experience the awakening of your soul.

WEEK THREE

<u>Diet</u> Continue to make the bulk of what you eat vegetables, fruits and grains. Look for foods in season. Strolling through a farmer's market and taking in the sights and smells of fruits and vegetables in season is a heady, sensual experience. If you buy more than you can eat - which I always seem to do because I'm so tempted by everything - you can share your bounty with friends.

<u>Exercise</u> If you are on the progressive walking regimen, up the duration of your walk to 15 minutes. Walk for five minutes. Stretch. Walk for

another 10 minutes. If you have a lake nearby, consider rowing as an occasional alternative to walking. The rhythm of the movement, the rippling of the water, the breeze blowing over the lake is almost hypnotic. It can be a tranquil, pleasurable way to get your daily exercise.

Therapeutic Breathing Continue with your chosen breathing exercise. If you have been faithfully doing your breathing session everyday, healing breaths are becoming comfortable and automatic. Use them throughout the day to relieve stress. If you're in your car waiting at an unusually long traffic light and you feel yourself getting impatient, take two or three long, slow, healing breaths. Tension will leave your body. You will bring yourself to a place where your stress level will drop but where you will still remain alert to the task of driving safely.

Heal Your Soul Journal for 15 minutes. If you have unfinished business with a person who has hurt or angered you, write about that. Mention how it came about and the feelings you experience when you think of the person or the incident. It is unnecessary to resolve this issue by talking to the person. You may choose to not associate with him again. Your goal is to dissolve the emotional anguish that you feel when thinking of him. You may need to write for more than one session to get rid of the feelings. Take as many sessions as you need to do this.

Serenity Having you ever danced by yourself? If you have, you know the feelings of absolute freedom you get when allowing yourself to flow with music. Choose a musical number that you just love. Find a space that is big enough to allow you to move freely. Stand quietly, take healing breaths and just listen. As the music fills your mind and your soul, begin to move with it. Go where ever it takes you. You may find, when the musical piece is over, that you don't want to stop. Ignore time. Continue to dance. You are healing your mind, your body and your spirit.

WEEK FOUR

Diet Continue to make the bulk of your food intake fruits, vegetables and grains. Your increased energy is due to eating healthier and avoiding foods high in fats and sugar. If you have heart disease, remember to reduce your intake of salt as recommended by your doctor. There are some salt substitutes on the market that provide similar taste results when sprinkled on foods. Try them until you find one you like. My husband who likes to cook, always uses his favorite substitute when a recipe calls for salt.

Exercise On the progressive walking regimen, extend your walk to twenty minutes. Begin by walking for seven minutes. Stop and stretch. Walk briskly for eight minutes. You should be breathing a little harder. Finish your walk at a more relaxed pace. This week your daily walking plan is to walk for seven minutes, stretch, walk briskly for eight minutes and do "cooling down" walking for five minutes.

If you are a jogger and have been running as your exercise activity, remember that running on concrete is hard on your feet and body and can have long-term adverse physical consequences. A better alternative is to drive to the nearest high school or college and run on their dirt track. This would be so much better for your body.

Therapeutic Breathing Continue your daily breathing session. The benefits that you gain while you are doing this exercise, extend throughout the day. You will find that your overall tension level is reduced and you have less chronic stress. You are also better able to handle unexpected problems that may arise. Remember to use one or two healing breaths whenever you need to keep yourself calm and focused.

Heal Your Soul Journal, visit with a friend or meet with a support group. A support group is the favorite healing milieu for many people with illness. Sharing fears and anxiety with others who have the same concerns is therapeutic. You may learn of various treatments, facilities and new technologies from the other people in the group. You will be there for each other through the ups and downs of your illnesses and treatments.

Serenity Continue with your favorite activity that gives you serenity. Try an art project. If you say, "I'm not an artist. I can't do art," think back to the time when you were a child. It is likely that you colored, painted, drew and made clay objects. You did it freely without judgment of your work. Release the child creator again. If you are really apprehensive about trying an art activity, buy some crayons and a coloring book and some blocks of clay from a toy store. When you are alone, color in your book. Mold your clay into simple shapes. After a few minutes of activity, you will realize how relaxed you feel. Tension will drain away and you will get lost in the moment.

Researchers have discovered that our inner reactions are the same when our bodies are healing and when we are doing art. The art activity can be as simple as coloring a picture or molding shapes out of clay. Use your imagination and create ways to make art. Try cutting pieces of sponge and dab paint on art paper. Look for art tools that look as if they'd be fun. I found some spinning tops that had colored pens for tips at the Museum of Modern Art store in New York City. Sitting and spinning them on paper and watching the different lines, shapes and spirals that emerge is fascinating. It lifts my spirits and makes me happy whenever I use them.

WEEK FIVE

Diet It is likely that without even thinking about losing, you are getting closer to your ideal weight. Because your body naturally move to the optimum condition for healing when you allow it to and you don't do things that will impede it's progress, eating healthy foods and eliminating fats and sugars gives it the opportunity to take care of itself. Continue to concentrate on fruits, vegetables and grains. If you are interested in becoming a strict vegan, eating no meat or dairy products, be sure you include beans, legumes and nuts for protein.

<u>Exercise</u> Increase your walk to 25 minutes. Walk for eight minutes. Stretch slowly. Walk briskly for twelve minutes, cool down with a slower pace for the last five minutes.

<u>Therapeutic Breathing</u> By this time, daily breathing sessions have become such a pleasant, calming part of your routine that you miss it if you have to skip a day. Don't fret or feel guilty. The benefits that you have gained will carry you through and you can resume on the following day.If there is a day when you don't have time to devote an entire 20 minutes to your session, do whatever you can. Even just five minutes will be beneficial. Do a full session on the next time.

<u>Heal Your Soul</u> Journal, visit a friend or meet with a support group. If you continue to be extremely anxious and are having difficulty resolving issues and concerns, consider seeing a therapist or meeting with a spiritual leader. These professionals are trained in guiding you through your healing process. Make sure that you choose someone with whom you are comfortable. You must have rapport with him or her before healing can take place. Don't be afraid to try several until you find the right one. Some therapists may even give you a free initial consultation to determine whether you are appropriate to work with each other.

<u>Serenity</u> Allot some time, this week to sit in the garden and enjoy nature. Listen to the birds, feel the breeze, watch the butterflies, smell the flowers. If it's winter, bundle up in warm clothing, make yourself a cup of coffee or hot chocolate, put on some warm mittens and sit on your porch or balcony under a cozy afghan. The different seasons stimulate different senses.

The variations can be interesting and exciting.

WEEK SIX

<u>Diet</u> Eating healthy is now part of your lifestyle. You automatically select foods that fuel your body and keep it running smoothly. If you occasionally want a piece of chocolate or other treat, go ahead and have it. Just make it a small one. And no more than one a week. Many people who are into the sixth week in their new eating regimen find that they no longer desire foods that do not support the body's functions. They crave apples or peaches for snacks. You have developed a way of eating that will keep your body functioning well for the rest of your life. If you become ill, you will recover faster. Your body will respond more quickly to treatment and medications.

<u>Exercise </u>Increase your walk to 30 minutes. Warm up at a leisurely pace for 10 minutes, stretch, walk briskly for 15 minutes and cool down at

a slower pace for five minutes. After this six-week period, you can continue daily 30 minute walks. If you want to increase the duration of your walks, do so incrementally a week at a time. Now that you have experienced the joy of walking, you may want to walk with friends or join a walking group. My favorite vacations are walking tours in places like Cornwall, England or on the John Muir Trail in California. With a well-chosen tour, the companionship is good, the food is scrumptious and stories, both historical and mythical, told by knowledgeable guides are fascinating.

Therapeutic Breathing Continue with your daily breathing sessions to keep your body strong and your mind resilient. Now that you have made healing breaths part of your lifestyle and breathing this way comes naturally, you can occasionally substitute other techniques for your regular method. Consider imagery. Refer to the section on imagery in chapter five for guidelines. My favorite imagery is of walking on the sandy expanse of a gentle ocean beach and letting the water lap over my feet as I walk along the shore.

Heal Your Soul   As you let go of past resentments and hurts and resolve emotionally charged unfinished business, you will notice how light you feel; how happiness seems to fill your being. You find yourself becoming more altruistic and noticing ways that you can help others. Give in to the urge to be there for others - friends, family and strangers alike. Be kind and compassionate. Share your happiness. When you reach out to people with compassion, they, in turn, reach out to others. We spread love and good will. The world becomes a better place.

Serenity   Regularly take part in activities that you have found pleasurable during this six-week period. Experience the joy that comes with being in the moment. Notice how calm and peaceful you feel while engaging in these activities. Revel in the knowledge that you are doing your part to maintain your health and participate in your healing.

Epilogue

A Final Walk With A Chinese Sage

My father died peacefully in bed at the age of ninety three. He had maintained residences in Northern California and in Hawaii, the state of his birth. He was in Hawaii at the time of his death.

When I'm on my daily walks I often remember my last walk with Dad. As usual, he was quiet, enjoying the warmth of the sun, the light breeze and the sounds of the ocean. I, as I often found myself doing, was chattering about my concerns.

"I ate too much last night. I also had dessert, which I know I shouldn't have had. Chocolate cake is so unhealthy."

Dad's reply was typical of his lifestyle and personal philosophy, " It's okay. Don't worry. You can eat anything you like ... pretty much do whatever you want. Just strive not to do anything in excess. Do everything in moderation ... savor every experience ... and be nice to people. Be kind and compassionate. Always be a person others can trust. Life will then be good. You will have found the keys to happiness, serenity and longevity."

BIBLIOGRAPHY

Borysenko, Joan & Miroslav. *The Power of the Mind To Heal*. Carson City, California: Hay House, Inc., 1994.

Brigham, Deirdre D. *Imagery For Getting Well*. New York/London: W.W. Norton & Co., Inc.,1994.

Chuckrow, Robert. *The Tai Chi Book*. Boston:YMAA Publishing Center, 1998.

Cohen, Misha Ruth. *The Chinese Way To Healing:Many Paths To Wholeness*. New York: The Berkeley Publishing Group, 1996.

(The) Dalai Lama & Cutler, Howard C. *The Art of Happiness*. New York:Riverhead Books,1998.

De Bary, Wm. Theodore, Chan Wing-Tsit & Watson, Burton. *Sources Of Chinese Tradition*. New York: Columbia University Press,1960.

Dong, Paul & Esser, Aristide H. *Chi Gong: The Ancient Way To Health*. New York: Marlowe & Company, 1990.

Dubovsky, Steven L. *Mind Body Deceptions*. New York/London:W.W. Norton & Co., Inc., 1997.

Gaynor, Mitchell L. *Sounds Of Healing*. New York: Broadway Books, 1999.

Golub, Marcia. *I'd Rather Be Writing*. Cincinnati, Ohio:Writer's Digest Books, 1999.

Grewal, J.K. & Sim, M.K. Chinese Diaphragmatic Breathing As An Adjunct to Relaxation:Effect On EEG.*Medical Psychotherapy*. 1989,*Vol 2*, 157-162.

Kemeny, M.E., Solomon, G., Morley, J., and Bennett, T. Psychoneuroimmunology. *Psychoendocrinology,* ed. Nemeroff, C.B. Boca Raton:CRC Press, 1992.

Murray, Elizabeth. *Cultivating Sacred Space.* San Francisco:Pomegranate, 1997.

Northrup, Christiane. *Women's Bodies, Women's Wisdom.* New York: Bantam Books, 1998.

Ornish, Dean. *Reversing Heart Disease.* New York: Ballantine Books, 1990.

Ornstein, Robert & Sobel, David. *Healthy Pleasures.* New York: Addison-Wesley Publishing Co., 1989.

Pearsall, Paul. *The Pleasure Prescription.* Alameda, California: Hunter House Publishers, 1996.

Pelletier, Kenneth R. Between mind and body: stress, emotions and health. *Mind Body Medicine,* eds. D. Goleman and J. Gurin. Yonkers, New York: Consumer Reports Books, 1993, pp. 20-38.

Reid, Daniel. *The Complete Book of Chinese Health and Healing.* New York: Barnes & Nobles, Inc. 1994.

Russell Peter. *Waking Up In Time.* Novato, California:Origin Press, 1992.

Sapolsky, Robert M. *Why Zebras Don't Get Ulcers.* New York:W.H. Freeman & Co. 1994.

Samuels, Michael & Lane, Mary Rockwood. *Creative Healing.* New York: HarperSanFrancisco, 1998.

Simonton, O. Carl. *Getting Well Again.* New York: Bantam Books, 1980.

Simpkins, C. Alexander and Annellen M. *Principles of Meditation.* Boston, Rutland and Tokyo:Charles E. Tuttle and Co., Inc., 1996.

Watts, Alan W. *The Meaning of Happiness.* New York:Harper & Row Publishers, 1940.

Weil, Andrew. *Spontaneous Healing.* New York:Alfred A. Knopf,Inc.,1995.

Weil, Andrew. *Eating Well For Optimum Health.* New York:Alfred A Knopf, 2000.

Williams, Tom. *The Complete Illustrated Guide To Chinese Medicine.* Dorset, Massachusetts, Queensland: Element Books, 1996.

Yang, Jwing Ming. *Muscle/Tendon Changing and Marrow/Brain Washing Chi Kung.* Jamaica Plain, Massachusetts: YMAA Publishing Center, 1989.

Yang, Jwing Ming. *Qigong For Arthritis.* Jamaica Plain, Massachusetts: YMAA Publishing Center, 1991.

_____. *Statistical Abstract of the United States.* Washington, DC: U.S. Bureau of the Census. U.S. Government Printing Office, 2002.